IC

It was all for the best, Kelly thought, when she pretended to be her troublesome sister Jayne and went off at their 'guardian' Joshua Brett's behest to Washington, so that he could keep an eye on her. But Joshua was a man to be reckoned with. What sort of punishment would he inflict when, inevitably, he discovered how Kelly had been deceiving him?

ICE STORM

BY

ANN COOPER

MILLS & BOON LIMITED
15–16 BROOK'S MEWS
LONDON W1A 1DR

First published 1982

Australian copyright 1982
Philippine copyright 1982
This edition 1983

© Ann Cooper 1982

ISBN 0 263 74062 5

Set in Monophoto Times 10 pt. solid
01–0183 - 60907

Made and printed in Great Britain by
Richard Clay (The Chaucer Press) Ltd,
Bungay, Suffolk

CHAPTER ONE

'YOU'RE not going, of course!' Kelly stared in horror. 'It's absolutely monstrous! Since when has Joshua Brett's word been law around here?'

Her sister shrugged. 'I really don't know how I can get out of it.'

'Let me see.' Kelly almost snatched the letter from Jayne's hand. *'In view of your latest escapade ...'* she read. 'Escapade!' Her amber eyes widened angrily. 'Does he think you get into these scrapes for fun?' She looked down at the letter again. *'... I think it would be advisable if you left the London social scene and spent a few quiet months in America ...'*

'He doesn't sound particularly angry,' Jayne ventured.

'Huh!' Kelly read the rest of the letter in silence. 'And he just expects you to go over to Washington, cap in hand almost, full of apologies and begging forgiveness ...'

'Perhaps, since Daddy died, he feels sort of responsible for us.'

Kelly folded the letter briskly and put it back in the envelope with the one-way airline ticket. 'How long is it since we've seen the great Joshua Brett?'

'Ages,' Jayne admitted.

'Exactly. And Daddy's been dead nearly three years. If he felt responsible for us he ought to have put in an appearance before now.' She marched to the window and gazed out over the Heath, and beyond, to the distant London skyline. Everything was wearing its grey winter overcoat. Thank heaven she was home for the Christmas vacation. Jayne could never have coped alone.

'If it hadn't been in the papers he would never have known,' Jayne said miserably. 'I suppose he must have been over here on one of his business trips.'

Kelly sighed, almost impatient with the sister who was three years older than herself. Three years! Heavens, at times Jayne was practically a child. If only she didn't have this dreadful track record with men.

She turned back from the window. '*So*,' she shrugged, 'it was in the papers. If your James hadn't been producing that play in the West End, the divorce wouldn't have made two lines in the local weekly. Just because you get involved with someone a bit well known, there's no need to persecute you . . .'

'The papers haven't persecuted me,' Jayne intervened.

'I don't mean them; I mean Joshua Brett.' Kelly stormed around the room, her dark hair swinging freely just above her shoulders. 'Who does he think he is? Doesn't he realise how awful it's been for you? The last thing you need right now is some heavy-handed bullying.'

'It isn't as simple as that.' Jayne fingered one of the tendrils of hair framing her face. Both the Osborn girls were of similar build and colouring, but whereas Kelly was forthright and strong, Jayne had an ethereal delicacy which drew her towards a man's protection; and drew them inextricably towards her. 'Glenda was on the phone,' she continued, 'before you arrived.'

'What did she want?' Their stepmother didn't often phone from Florida, it had to be important. Kelly sensed trouble.

'She—she thinks I ought to go over to Washington.' Jayne's hands fluttered prettily.

'You're joking!'

Jayne shook her head. 'She's—Glenda's—got some sort of business deal going through. She wants to buy a beauty farm down there.'

'What's that got to do with you?' asked Kelly, flopping down on one of the settees and curling her feet beneath her.

'She wants to borrow quite a bit of money from Joshua . . .'

'Don't tell me,' Kelly interrupted, 'so if Joshua says jump, we all have to jump—right?' she added fiercely.

'I guess so,' replied her sister.

'I still don't understand *why*!' Kelly was on her feet again, pacing the spacious living room of the Osborns' Hampstead flat. 'Surely there was plenty of money when she sold Daddy's company. Why does she have to borrow money—and least of all from *him*?'

Jayne hesitated. 'It's—something about all the money being tied up, I think. Daddy's will was pretty tight. There's our allowances—and Glenda's—but I don't think she had much else to play with. It's all been invested for future growth.'

Kelly couldn't argue with that. Their father had been a shrewd business man, acutely conscious that as his second wife had been so much younger, she could possibly be a widow for a great many years. Kelly sighed and stared out of the window again. It was beginning to get dark, there was only a week left to Christmas . . .

'Glenda's always wanted a beauty farm,' Jayne smoothed the skirt of her soft pink dress, 'ever since we've known her.'

'I know.' Kelly sighed again. Glenda might not have been a perfect stepmother, but then who could blame her? She was only thirty-five now, she had been in her late twenties when she had married Stuart Osborn; she still had a life of her own to live. The two sisters stared at each other. If only Jayne hadn't been cited in this divorce—and it wasn't the first time . . . But there was no point in 'if onlys'. Kelly marched through the kitchen and made them both some coffee.

It was out of the question, Jayne couldn't possibly go to Washington. Kelly could remember Joshua Brett from the old days when he had worked for their father's aero company. He had been head of the design team—a brilliant young engineer—and then he had formed his own company to design equipment for astro-navigation. Now, six years later, he was head of the internationally known Space Design U.K. He had offices in London and Washington, and you didn't progress that quickly unless you were brilliant, resourceful—and ruthless. He had left her father's company with Stuart Osborn's blessing—they had remained friends until the end. But Kelly had never felt easy in his company—his social visits to the Osborn home had always been accompanied with humiliation, nerves, and she had always wanted to get away.

'Joshua was Glenda's boy-friend, wasn't he?' she said, carrying the mugs through to the living room. 'I mean, before he introduced her to Daddy.'

Jayne nodded. 'But I don't think they are now—I mean, she wouldn't be in this state about keeping him happy.'

Kelly put the mugs down on the glass and chrome coffee table. 'Ever wondered why she chose Daddy—a man twenty years older than herself?'

'I suppose she loved him. You're not suggesting it was because of his money?'

Kelly shook her head. 'I'll tell you what I think,' she said, sipping her coffee. 'If you had the choice between an older man who was loving and gentle and thought the world of you, and a young man who was attractive—but also a ruthless, single-minded business man who would only give you a small part of his attention—which would you choose?'

'I see what you mean.' Jayne looked more unhappy than ever.

'And if he was like that six years ago, what on earth is he going to be like now? Jayne, you can't go—he'll crucify you!'

The older sister wrung her hands. 'I don't see what choice I have. Daddy would have wanted . . .'

'There's no need to say that.' Kelly picked up a magazine and threw it down again. 'Look, you don't actually *want* to go, do you?'

'Of course not.' Jayne picked up her own coffee, her long red nails a vivid contrast against the delicate china mug. 'In fact—well, I've sort of been invited away for Christmas,' she studied the flowery design on the mug, 'to the—er—Seychelles . . .'

Kelly's eyes widened. 'And you can sit there and even *contemplate* going over to Washington? Really, Jayne, write to Joshua—ring him up. Does Glenda know about the Seychelles?'

'It's not quite as simple as that,' Jayne began. 'You see, there's this man . . .'

'Oh no!' Kelly bounced off the settee and began marching about the room again. 'You're not getting yourself involved with another man already?' Then she tried to control her anger. 'Perhaps you'd better go to Washington—Joshua Brett can't actually kill you,' but even to her own ears she didn't sound convinced.

Jayne burst into tears and Kelly felt dreadful.

'You don't understand,' she sobbed. 'It's all right for you, you're up at university with all your friends, and I'm here on my own, trying to become an actress. And I'm not like you, Kelly. I need someone—I'm not independent.'

'I know, love. I'm sorry.' Kelly gave her sister a hug and mopped her up. 'It's that damn man,' she said, resuming her seat and reaching for the coffee again. 'It's all his fault. What right does he think he has to sit and judge you? This fellow—the one who wants to take you away for Christmas—do you . . .?' The rest of the question hung in the air.

'Love him?' Jayne ventured. 'I—think so.'

'You *think*!' Her sister looked tearful again, so Kelly relented.

'But what are we going to do?' Jayne went on, wiping her nose. 'I don't want to let Glenda down. I *dare* not—because it would be dreadful if she sold this flat . . .'

'Would she?' said Kelly sharply.

'She says she'll have to—to raise the money—if Joshua won't give her a loan.' Jayne sniffed miserably. 'But I was so looking forward to going to the Seychelles—and the thought of Joshua Brett scares me to death.'

Kelly was deep in her own thoughts for quite a while. 'How long exactly is it since Joshua Brett saw us? Saw us both, I mean?'

Jayne shrugged. 'He was at the wedding—that's six years. And he couldn't get to Daddy's funeral because he was in California for some space probe thing . . .'

'Huh! See what I mean,' Kelly interrupted. 'Couldn't take a few days off from his precious work.' Then slowly a gleam of mischief glinted in her eyes.

'What's the matter?' asked Jayne.

But Kelly didn't answer. Instead, she dashed into her bedroom and pulled out a large box from under the bed.

'Who's that?' she asked, coming back into the living room and waving an old photograph at Jayne.

'You,' said her sister.

'And who's this?' Kelly was enjoying herself.

'That's me, when I was at Court School.'

'Look alike, don't we?' Kelly prompted.

Jayne was suddenly appalled. 'You wouldn't *dare*,' she breathed.

'Why not?'

'If he found out . . .?'

'But he isn't going to find out, is he?' Kelly propped up both pictures against their mugs. '*Jayne* Osborn, thirteen years old. *Kelly* Osborn, thirteen years old. Either of those girls could have grown up to look like me.'

'But I was sixteen at the wedding,' reminded Jayne. 'Much more mature.' So Kelly rummaged in her box and found a photo of Jayne taken a few years later.

'It gets better,' said Kelly, studying the picture of Jayne at sixteen. She had still worn her long hair down to her shoulders in those days, and there was a sturdiness about her then that she had lost in the following years. 'If that's who Joshua Brett remembers as Jayne Osborn, then he's going to have no problem believing I'm you.'

'I couldn't let you.'

Kelly grinned. 'That's what sisters are for.'

'It's a bit drastic.'

'It would be even more drastic if you went. That's decided.' She put the lid firmly back on the box. 'Honestly, I don't mind—Joshua Brett won't hurt me whatever he says or does. I tell you what,' her sherry eyes twinkled, 'I'll ring him—now.'

Jane looked astounded. 'What time is it over there?'

'Midday, I think.' Kelly picked up the phone and Jayne opened her letter again and looked at the international phone number printed at the top. He had written on his company's notepaper, his secretary had obviously typed it. Which proved that this wasn't a personal matter for him—just another business arrangement that had to be dealt with.

Kelly was halfway through the string of numbers when she slammed down the phone again. 'The newspaper report,' she gasped hurriedly, 'was there a picture of you? He just *might* have seen it!'

There was! Jayne rushed to get it and handed it to Kelly with downcast eyes.

Twenty-year-old marriage ends . . . was the headline. Kelly hadn't realised it had been as bad as that. And it wasn't as if the romance had worked out, she knew Jayne hadn't been seeing this particular fellow for several months now. This was a picture of them both taken at a night club some time ago. He looked about forty-five, facing straight into the camera, Jayne was more or less side view, wearing one of her clinging dresses. They were dancing, her dark hair was in its usual topknot. It wasn't a good photograph; Kelly would hardly have recognised her.

'No problem there.' She tossed the paper aside and picked up the phone again. If there was the slightest chance that Joshua had seen that picture he would still be none the wiser.

'Supposing Glenda finds out?' asked Jayne, tugging at Kelly's arm.

'Why should she? She's set fair down in Florida—you know how she hates the cold weather, and I expect Washington is pretty chilly now.' Jayne didn't look convinced. 'Look,' Kelly added firmly, 'it's a risk I'm just going to have to take.' Suddenly it had become very important that she should take her sister's place. Why? 'You need a rest,' she continued lightly. 'You're looking a bit peaky—I thought that the moment I arrived.'

'Do I?' Jayne dashed into her own room to inspect the damage. Kelly sighed with relief—that settled it, there would be no more opposition from Jayne.

She picked up the letter again and dialled the numbers. The connection sounded hollow and squeaky, then a few seconds later it began to ring.

'Space Design U.K.,' announced a cheerful voice. 'May I help you?'

Kelly swallowed. 'I want to speak to Joshua Brett,' and when she was asked who was calling, she crossed her fingers and said, 'Osborn—Jayne Osborn.'

The transfer was made with the speed of light, there wasn't time for Kelly to think before a firm, crisp voice said, 'Joshua Brett.'

Kelly was glad she was alone in the room. 'This is Jayne,' she said firmly. 'Jayne Osborn . . .'

'Just a moment,' he said, before she could go further, and she was pretty sure he had his hand over the mouthpiece and was talking to someone. Kelly drummed her fingers. Didn't he realise she was paying for this call? 'You've received my letter?' he said suddenly, 'and the ticket?'

Kelly blinked. 'Er—yes.'

'Good. I'll meet you at Dulles, your flight gets in about tea-time.'

'Dallas?' Texas? Wasn't she supposed to be going to Washington?

'I said *Dulles*,' he sounded impatient. 'It's the international airport here. I'll be there to pick you up myself.'

'Terrific,' Kelly muttered.

'What?'

'Er—nothing.'

'Bring plenty of warm clothes—and some Wellington boots.'

'Whatever for?' she asked.

'It is winter, Jayne, even here.' She heard a buzz on his telephone module. 'I have a call coming in—I'll see you Monday. I presume your visa is in order.'

Kelly had a moment's panic, then she remembered

that both sisters had indefinite visas obtained for a visit to Glenda last summer.

'Of course,' she answered coolly.

'Good. Goodbye.' He put the phone down.

Kelly replaced her own receiver and found to her amazement that her hands were trembling. She tried to stuff them in her jeans pockets so that Jayne wouldn't see.

'What did he say?' asked her sister from the doorway.

Kelly shrugged and wondered why her knees felt strangely weak. 'Nothing much—he didn't seem surprised that you'd agreed to go.'

'What did he sound like?'

'Disagreeable.'

Jayne bit her lip. 'You're sure you're doing the right thing?'

Kelly grinned. 'Sure I'm sure. I haven't met a man yet that I couldn't handle. Once they know you're not going to fall at their feet they either treat you as a friend or keep out of your way.'

'I'll never understand you,' Jayne whispered.

And I'll never understand how you let men take advantage of you, thought Kelly, but she decided not to say so.

Two days to prepare for a trip to America! It was ludicrous, but at least it didn't give Kelly the chance to change her mind. And now the decision was made, Jayne threw herself into helping her sister get ready.

'You're not really going to take *this*,' she announced, holding up an ancient plaid dressing-gown that was a relic of Kelly's schoolgirl days. She went through the rest of Kelly's clothes then, discarding most of them to the bedroom floor. 'I refuse to let you wear these while you're supposed to be me,' she shuddered, and Kelly sat on her bed and rocked with laughter. Trust Jayne to worry about that at a time like this!

And after the clothes had been sorted out and Kelly had promised to take mostly Jayne's, she had to learn how to put her hair up in a topknot, because the topknot had been in the newspaper photo. And if she was supposed to be Jayne she also ought to *think* herself into the part—or so her sister told her.

Kelly did her best. Two days, and one of them Sunday, hadn't been long to buy a few odds and ends, get her hair trimmed and telephone her friends to change the Christmas arrangements.

'You're not coming?' Her room-mate from university had sounded really sorry. A whole crowd of them were going to spend Christmas on her parents' farm.

'You won't really miss me,' Kelly laughed. 'It's just that this trip has come up unexpectedly.'

'Alan will be disappointed,' said her friend.

Kelly pulled a face. 'Not for long, if I know him. I'll send you a postcard—see you all in January!' Funny, she had almost forgotten Alan these past few days. Not that he really counted—he was just one of a string of male friends; there was nothing remotely serious between them—she would send him a postcard too.

But now the two days were past. Her suitcases were locked and ready, and she had booked an alarm call for six-thirty the following morning.

Tomorrow she would be in Washington—tomorrow she would see Joshua Brett for the first time in six years ... She had a restless night, dreaming of a long hot summer's afternoon years and years ago. Her father, Glenda and Jayne had been there, having tea in the garden under the chestnut tree at the house in Surrey ... and Joshua had come to say goodbye. He had flirted with Glenda and the sixteen-year-old Jayne, but to him Kelly had been merely a child and he had teased her for continually winding her hair behind her ear. The rattle of tea-cups, the buzzing bees and a butterfly dancing around their heads on that sultry afternoon. The dream was as clear and painful as the reality had been. Kelly had sat apart, silent, mutinous, humiliated. One day she would grow up and show them all ...

The phone rang and she was instantly awake, stumbling through the sitting-room and snatching up the receiver.

'Thank you,' she mumbled, before the operator could

speak, but there was no one there for a moment, and then a woman's voice said, 'Kelly?'

It was Glenda.

'Er—yes.' She sank on the settee and peered at her watch. Typical. Glenda never did understand time zones.

'Is Jayne there?' Her stepmother's American accent always sounded more pronounced over the phone; she had lived nearly ten years in England, but had never lost it.

'She's asleep. It's very early, Glenda.'

'Is it?' It was a good line, Kelly could detect an edge of irritation in Glenda's voice. 'I've just had a call from Joshua,' she continued. 'He says she's coming over to-morrow . . .'

'Today—yes, that's right,' Kelly explained.

'She ought to get out of London, it won't do any harm. She's gone too far this time, Kelly. Joshua is really mad!'

'I don't see that it's any of his business,' Kelly began automatically.

Glenda sighed. 'Joshua has made it his business—that's enough.'

'Jayne is perfectly within her rights to refuse, Glenda. She isn't a child. He doesn't have any legal right.'

'You tell her it's for her own good.' Glenda's voice sounded harder. 'If she messes me up with Joshua I'll have to get the money elsewhere. And I guess she's already told you how that will be.'

'I don't want you to sell this flat, any more than she does,' Kelly said tightly.

'Good. Then you make damn sure Jayne gets on that plane. I don't want her running out at the last minute. I'm holding you responsible, Kelly. I know you're the younger—but you've got,' she hesitated, 'you've got your father's spirit. Use it to keep Jayne in line.'

Glenda sounded desperate. Kelly didn't like it. A desperate woman could be dangerous. She forced her anger back and asked if there was any chance of Glenda coming to Washington over Christmas.

'No way, honey. I've got things all nicely tied up down here.' There wasn't much more to say after that.

Kelly put the phone down and stared thoughtfully at her father's photograph on the bookshelf. He had been a strong man with a shock of white hair in later life. His face was firm and kind, yet he had shown great self-discipline and determination. Maybe that was what Glenda recognised when she looked at Kelly. But almost against his character, her father had had a weakness for helpless, feminine women. First their mother, sweet and timid—like Jayne. And then Glenda, who hadn't been sweet and timid but who had nevertheless craved protection and security. Was this beauty farm her idea of security? Jayne had been right; their father would have wanted them to help . . . Help Glenda? Or help themselves to keep their home? What did it matter? Either way Kelly was committed.

The phone rang—it was her alarm call. The last doubt vanished. She was on her way to America!

It was a good flight. There were a lot of children travelling alone and Kelly guessed they were flying out for the holidays to join British families working in Washington. She was glad that she had never been separated from her family in that way. Even when their mother died Stuart had kept both girls at the local day-school and had employed a housekeeper. Until Glenda came—yet Kelly had never been jealous. Had Jayne? Was that why she had gone off the rails? Who could say?

They were about to touch down at Boston and Kelly fastened her seat-belt for the landing. They had been flying down over the wastes of Canada; nothing but vast frozen isolation, but now as the plane flew over Boston harbour, Kelly held her breath in delight.

The plane stopped and beyond her window there was nothing but the water and a distant line of houses. It looked cold and still out there. Nothing moved. There were no cars, no people—not even a ripple on the water. And the light was terrific; a clear blue light painted yellow with the afternoon sun. There was a knife-edge clarity, a sharpness, that Kelly had never seen before. It was almost unreal; timeless. She could easily expect a dug-out canoe and men in fur hats to come paddling into view!

Then the Boston passengers came on board and the empty seat next to her own was taken by a rather nice-looking man who introduced himself and seemed happy to chat for the rest of the trip.

He tried to make a date with Kelly, but she said she wasn't sure of her plans. He took the hint, but didn't seem to mind in the slightest, so they automatically got off the plane together when it touched down at Dulles. After Immigration he found a trolley and they waited for their cases together.

'Someone meeting you?' he asked, although she had already told him. A friend of the family . . .' And then the cases began arriving and they had to keep a sharp lookout. His came first, but he seemed quite happy to wait for hers. Kelly was beginning to feel a bit sick. She was probably hungry, she never could eat much on planes . . . and then her luggage came out. 'The tan one,' she pointed, 'and the green . . .' and he hauled them off the merry-go-round and stacked them on his trolley. 'It's very kind of you,' she said, but felt a bit uncertain.

He smiled easily. 'Never know—your friend might not turn up.'

Some hope, she thought, as they both automatically laughed together. They passed through Customs almost without stopping, and then the doors slid open for them and they were through to the outside world.

Faces, a mixture of anxiety and boredom, were watching every passenger as they appeared, but she didn't see anyone she recognised.

'That's my driver,' said her travelling companion. 'D'you see your friend?' and Kelly shook her head. 'Perhaps I can give you a lift somewhere?'

They stood in the arrivals lounge, it was small and practically deserted after the chaos at Heathrow. 'I don't think so—I'd better wait,' Kelly began, and then a firm hand grasped her arm.

'Jayne? Jayne Osborn?' And Kelly turned round and stared up at the man she knew to be Joshua Brett. He was tall and dark, his thick sheepskin jacket making him seem almost a giant. He glanced at the American with cold, shrewd eyes. If looks could kill he ought to be frozen to death.

'Thank you for your help,' said Kelly, turning back to him and extending her hand. 'I hope you have a successful business trip.' She was glad there was something automatic she could say, because suddenly she couldn't think very straight. Joshua was taking her cases off the trolley and the American was taking her hand and saying a reluctant goodbye.

She couldn't think straight, because time had lied to her and she hadn't been prepared for Joshua Brett to be the most lethally attractive man she had ever met.

The American seemed to vanish, he was forgotten for ever, and as Joshua led the way to the escalator she had to run to keep up with him. He had long, easy strides and seemed to be carrying her bulky cases without even noticing them.

Heads turned as they passed, and Kelly could understand why. He was the sort of man who would always get noticed—big, powerful, with an aggressive, dynamic personality that she guessed could be felt at a hundred paces.

They were at street level now and as the doors slid open an icy blast caught Kelly right between the eyes. They crossed the road, Joshua walking, Kelly running; the car park was almost empty. Joshua began loading her gear into a long black car that looked new and extremely expensive.

'Did you have a good flight?' he asked at last, as she stood shivering slightly, but whether from cold or tension she couldn't be sure.

'Okay.' The wind whipped an escaped strand of hair across her face and as she wound it behind her ear he glanced at her quickly. In less than a second she knew he had taken in every minute detail; her dark hair in its topknot, her silver fox jacket with its collar up to protect

her ears, long boots covering shapely legs. A neat figure
. . . He saw everything, and some instinct told Kelly that
he liked what he saw.

He unlocked his door and all the catches sprang up
automatically. Kelly climbed inside, relieved to get out
of the wind. Joshua slid in beside her and every nerve in
her body reacted against him. She could feel his eyes on
her again. Did he know who she really was? Did he
guess?

He started the car, and the automatic transmission
glided them smoothly forward.

'You must be tired,' he remarked, pulling up at the
ticket barrier, but he hadn't parked long enough, so
there was nothing to pay.

'It's been a long day,' she admitted, casting him an
uncertain, sideways glance. Why uncertain? This was the
Joshua Brett she had known for years. Only it wasn't,
was it? Or at nineteen was she looking with different eyes?
She must have been mad—*mad*—to suggest this crazy
scheme. It wasn't going to work. *This* Joshua Brett would
be a hard man to fool . . . Panic throbbed through her.

'Did you make arrangements to see that fellow again?'
he asked, when they had driven along in silence for a
while. Kelly was calmer now and something in his cold,
imperious tone made her see red.

'And what if I did?' she said, tossing her head.

'Cancel it.'

'No.'

Without warning, he swung into a parking lot—it was
the kind of out-of-town place commuters left their cars
to travel the rest of the way with a friend. The car gently
rocked to a halt on its springs and he swung round to
face her. One arm went along the back of her seat and
the flesh down her neck quivered.

'I haven't brought you over here to get out of one
mess and straight into another.' The strong lines of his
face were drawn with contempt. Had she really thought
him handsome? Never! 'While you're here you'll *go*
where I say, *do* what I say—and only see those whom I
permit.'

Her eyes widened. 'You're joking,' she said bravely, although her knees were trembling.

'No, Jayne, I'm not joking—you'll discover I rarely joke.'

Jayne! He had called her Jayne. That was something.

He started the car again and pulled out into the traffic. No argument—and he obviously hadn't expected it.

For once Kelly couldn't argue. She was speechless. Did he really think he could keep her a prisoner? Hah! What a good thing she wasn't the real Jayne!

CHAPTER TWO

THE traffic grew heavier as they neared Washington and the Capital Beltway was really busy. But they soon saw the sign to Mclean and Joshua left the fast moving lanes and headed for the peace and seclusion of the fashionable suburbs.

The late afternoon sun played games through the tall bare trees. Kelly saw houses nestling in wooded hollows, while others sat in spacious companionship with their neighbours. The sky was blue and very bright, and the white houses with their sculptured, classical porticoes bounced back the sun and the cold, sharp air and suggested warmth and elegance within. There were very few people about, which was a reminder of exactly how cold it was out there. Cold enough for snow. Kelly wondered if they would have a white Christmas.

The journey had taken about half an hour, during which time they had both remained silent. Kelly wasn't used to travelling in silence, yet some inner caution told her to do so now. She wasn't sure yet how to handle Joshua Brett. He made her feel strange and prickly. She still didn't like him, that much was evident, even if he did look like a prize specimen of the male.

He was a big man, tall and athletically built, but it wasn't just that which she found unnerving. He was an unusual mixture of cool sophistication, which showed in the immaculate, well-fitting suit he was wearing beneath the sheepskin jacket. But even deeper down lay a hard toughness. She couldn't see it, exactly, but she was aware of it. It was a good thing the car was big and there was no chance that he would accidentally brush against her. She could still feel the pressure of his fingers on her arm when they had first met. Or was it her imagination?

At last they pulled into a wide driveway and the sweep

of lawn was smooth enough for a bowling green. The gracious lines of the large white house made it appear almost majestic. Kelly couldn't help feeling impressed. The car stopped at a flight of shallow stone steps that led up to an imposing double front door. There was a Christmas wreath enhancing the general air of wealth and elegance. Anyone else would have found it all most welcoming, but there was nothing welcoming about Joshua as he climbed out of the car and retrieved her luggage from the boot. As he did so the front door was opened by a black manservant whom Joshua introduced as William. But they had hardly completed the introductions and the front door had just been closed behind them, when the hall suddenly was full of people. Or full of women, to be precise.

A pretty blonde teenager in tight pants and sloppy sweater appeared from one room with a, 'Hi, Joshua—had a good trip?' Whereupon another door opened and a very cool lady with blonde upswept hair and a neat suit said, 'There's been a call from Pasadena . . .' and Joshua disappeared with her, leaving William to show Kelly to her room.

'I'm Rosey,' said the youngster, coming along behind. 'From next door. I guess you're Jayne.' She followed Kelly right into her bedroom.

'Thank you, William. Yes, tea would be lovely,' and Kelly flopped on the bed, bewildered by it all. What were all these women doing here?

'You staying long?' Rosey wandered round the room touching the sparkling surfaces. It was a nice room— cool and light. The furniture was white with trimmings of gold. Only the bedcover and curtains had any colour; they were a pretty sprigged green.

'I don't know how long I'll be here,' said Kelly, getting up and finding the adjoining bathroom. Not bad— in fact it was all quite luxurious.

'Work, do you?' Rosey was inspecting her cases for interesting labels.

'I'm an actress.' Well, she had to start some time and she might as well practise on this girl.

Rosey's eyes lit up. 'Are you famous?'

Kelly heaved one of the cases on to the bed. 'If I were you wouldn't have to ask, would you? And anyway, who are you?' Two could play at the interrogation game.

'Oh, I'm a friend of Joshua's.' Rosey tossed back her hair; it was very long and straight. She reminded Kelly of a little elf. 'You one of his girl-friends?'

The catches of Kelly's case sprang open. *One* of them? How many did the wretched man have? 'No,' she said tightly. 'He's just a friend of the family.' Friend! Huh, devil incarnate, more like.

'Known him long?' Rosey's questions seemed never-ending.

'All my life,' which was an exaggeration. But Kelly was prone to exaggerate when she was cross. 'Now if you don't mind I'd like to freshen up.'

'Sure—see you later.'

But not, thought Kelly, if I see you first. What was Joshua doing letting a child like that roam about the place? Or was he switched on by the Lolita image? And who was that blonde downstairs?

She unpacked and had a shower, but it was still only six o'clock; it felt more like midnight. Her tea had been brought up when she had been in the bathroom, and now she sipped it with relief while padding around the thick white carpet slowly putting on her clean under-wear. The large double bed looked so inviting and pretty in its sprigged quilt that reached the floor. But she mustn't lie down, that would be fatal. The quickest way to adjust to the time difference was not to sleep until the proper time.

She was tempted to put on a comfortable skirt and jumper, but another look in the mirror told her it would be a mistake. Right now she looked like Kelly, so she sighed and sat down on the stool and struggled with her hair. She had been practising for days and the topknot was soon secure. Then she found a lacy woollen dress that was so delicate and slinky that it made her feel rather nice. Jayne sure had a fantastic wardrobe, and as she would hardly need winter clothes in the Indian Ocean, she had been more than generous when helping Kelly to pack.

She hung up Jayne's fur jacket in the long fitted wardrobe, and ran her fingers along the line of unfamiliar clothes. It must be quite fun being Jayne. Then she dismissed the idea. *Fun* wasn't the right word.

It was dark now, and as Kelly wandered out on to the landing, she saw that lamps had been switched on. There was glass everywhere—glass side tables, glass table lamps with large white shades. The fittings and trimmings were gold. She walked, or rather drifted, down the curved staircase. In the hall there was a display of lush green ferns and vivid red poinsettias. If this was Washington, she liked it!

Kelly found her way to the drawing-room where more tea and cakes were laid out on a trolley. There was no one about, so she took a plate and helped herself to a cookie. As she did, there was the sound of voices out in the hall. The front door closed and a moment later Joshua came striding into the room.

'I hope you didn't wait for me,' he said conventionally. 'I've been away over the weekend and one or two important things have come up.'

Kelly sat down on one of the large settees. She felt instantly on edge and was annoyed by it. He wasn't wearing the sheepskin jacket now, and the dark business suit and sparkling white shirt made him look even more crisp and efficient.

'Was that your secretary?' she heard herself ask.

He was pouring himself some tea. 'One of them.'

'Do you often work at home?'

He sat himself down in one of the white leather armchairs and stretched out his long legs. 'Not often—depends.' She could feel his eyes on her; on the smooth knitted dress with its lacy top.

'There was another girl here just now . . .' she began.

'William's sent her home.' Joshua was almost smiling. 'Rosey seems to live here.'

'Is there anyone else living here that I ought to know about?' she asked nastily.

Anger darkened his face. 'Not at the moment.' Then he smiled harshly and there was something dark and satanic in those incredible eyes. 'There's just the two of us,' he purred.

'And William.'

'He doesn't live in.' His voice was icy again, quite matter-of-fact. 'What's the matter, Jayne? Don't you like the idea of being alone in a house with a man? I would have thought you would be quite used to it by now.'

'Don't you speak to me like that!' Kelly bounced off her seat and put her plate back on the trolley with a clatter. 'I didn't come all this way to be insulted!'

'If your father was still alive he'd do more than that— he'd give you a damn good hiding!'

'Don't you speak of Daddy like that,' she gasped. 'He wouldn't have dreamed of hitting us!'

'Then he did you no favour, little lady.'

Kelly glared at him. 'This is the twentieth century, you know.'

'And that's supposed to excuse what you did?'

'I didn't come here with a bagful of excuses,' Kelly retorted. 'What happened—happened,' she shrugged, 'and it isn't for you or anyone to sit in judgment.'

He took a sip of tea. Strong, well-shaped fingers coiled aggressively around the fine bone china.

'You've been in the gossip columns for as long as I can remember,' he exaggerated. '*Three* producers, *one* television director, *two* divorce cases even before this latest affair that really made the big time. You haven't done six months' work in the past four years.' His strong suntanned face was transformed with stern lines of disapproval and contempt. 'And you say I shouldn't sit in judgment!' He laughed harshly. 'It's about time someone did, Jayne, before you do any more harm. Before you really get hurt yourself.'

'And since when would that worry you?' Kelly retorted. 'You're not my guardian. I don't have to do

anything you say. I could walk out of here tomorrow
. . .'

'You have the fare, of course.' He was watching her
carefully, his eyes strangely enigmatic as if he was
assessing an opponent. If he knew the truth he would
have a fit. Kelly found the thought comforting.

'I'm not exactly broke—I do have an allowance,' she
reminded him grandly. Not that hers could stretch to
air fares at the moment, but he wasn't to know that.

'I think the least said about your allowance the better.'
Joshua Brett stared down his nose at her. A dark curl
licked across his temple; Kelly was amazed that she
noticed.

'I don't know what you mean.' She stood very tall
and straight. It was what Jayne would have done.

'You know perfectly well what I mean. When Glenda
sold your father's company it might have left you all
with independent means, but money doesn't grow on
trees. It needs careful handling, sound investing—not to
mention wise spending. You've done nothing but fritter
it away without making the slightest attempt to earn
some extra money if you needed it.' His eyes were like
ice. 'It can't go on, Jayne.'

'Since when have you known so much about the
Osborn affairs?' Outwardly she was incensed, but inwardly
she was furious with Jayne if what he said was true.

'I've known all about the Osborn affairs since your
stepmother asked me to be her financial adviser.'

'Financial adviser,' Kelly repeated sarcastically. 'Is
that what you call it?'

'Call what?'

'Your friendship with Glenda.' Maybe she had been
wrong. Maybe they were lovers again.

His anger sharpened. 'My relationship with your
stepmother has nothing to do with you—except insofar
as it relates to your allowance.' There was a dark edge
to his voice that told Kelly to drop the subject.

'Does that mean that you can stop it?' She refused to
be silenced—this was important. What right had he to
interfere?

'Of course I can't stop your allowance,' he said angrily. 'But it means that I shall advise Glenda not to authorise any more advances. You'll receive your allowance on every quarter day and not a minute before. If you run out of money that's your tough luck!'

'Glenda *agreed*?' That wasn't like her; she enjoyed spending money, enjoyed seeing other people spend it, too. Not that Kelly had ever asked for an advance, it wouldn't have occurred to her. That was why she didn't have much money left as it was over half-way through December.

'Of course she agreed,' Joshua began, sliding back the mesh fireguard and throwing another log on to the blaze. 'It surprises you?'

Kelly laughed cynically, remembering. 'Of course it doesn't surprise me. You hold all the cards at the moment, don't you? Glenda would say "yes" to anything right now.'

He stood up suddenly and brushed the dust from his hands. He had broad shoulders and long, powerful thighs, which meant that his clothes fitted in all the right places. Just for a moment Kelly's eyes were riveted. The dark trousers and jacket suited him. Black was the colour of night—of the unknown—of fear. The severe lines accentuated his shape and the blackness accentuated his suntan. But it did something else as well; it marked him as a man with no time in his life for warmth and colour. Ruthless. Hard. These were the words that sprang to mind when you looked at Joshua Brett. She felt trapped.

'I think we'd better get one thing perfectly clear right from the start,' he said coolly, and Kelly had to drag her eyes up to his face. 'You're here because you are Stuart Osborn's daughter. You would have come regardless of Glenda's little business deal.'

'Is that a fact?' He was surprised at Kelly's tone. Good. Because she had a few surprises of her own as well. 'I'd like to get one thing perfectly clear as well,' she said, marching across the thick carpet to stand directly in front of him. 'I only came *because* of Glenda's

little business deal, as you call it. It might only be little
to you, but it's important to her. She's always been
talking about a beauty farm ever since I've known her.
Okay, so she isn't my mother,' Kelly added, holding up
her hand to silence whatever it was that he was about to
say, 'but my father married her.' She laughed suddenly.
'So perhaps you're right—perhaps I am only here because I'm Stuart Osborn's daughter. But I'm here because we Osborn women stick together, too!'

She was finished. Her dark amber eyes were alive and
bright, her whole body bounced with rage and some
other disturbing affliction. This was a fight, and
suddenly Kelly knew she was enjoying it. Joshua was
enjoying it too; his eyes responded with a crackle of
admiration almost in spite of himself. But not for
long.

'A very good performance, my dear Jayne,' he
drawled. 'I really am most surprised that you haven't
had more success on the stage.' His eyes were cool again
as Kelly swept past. She could have killed him.

Supper was a plate and fork affair eaten off their laps
while listening to the stereo. William had gone; the
house that had been full of people when Kelly had
arrived was now empty. Joshua had spent two hours
working in his study and Kelly had tried to read in her
room; and just about managed to keep awake. They
hadn't seen each other until Joshua had called her down
to supper. And she had come down reluctantly. There
was a tension between them that she couldn't quite
name. It went deeper than hate.

Kelly chased the lobster around the plate, her appetite
gone as she glanced at him beneath her lashes. The dark
business suit had been replaced by close-fitting slacks
and a polo sweater, both black. His hair was very dark
brown, almost black, as well; dark, dangerous and unfathomable. At his feet was an open briefcase and it
looked as if he planned to carry on working in here
after he had finished his meal. She had heard him talking
to William earlier, and apparently his trip over the

weekend had been purely business. He had arrived back
in Washington only an hour or so before her own plane
had landed. Yet he didn't look like a man who had
worked long hard hours and had secret talks with space
men; he looked cool and remote; a man of ice—yet
utterly relaxed.

'Glenda—when she phoned you—did she tell you
what I had in mind?'

Kelly was so surprised at the sudden sound of his
voice that she almost dropped her fork. What was the
matter with her? Why was she so jumpy? 'Er—Glenda?
No. She just said you'd decided to play the heavy
father.'

His eyes crackled. 'Yes—and it's a pity I didn't decide
to do so a good deal earlier. All this—behaviour—it's
got to stop, Jayne. Look at you—you're no more than a
child.'

'I'm twenty-two years old,' Kelly lied.

'Hah! You look seventeen—but we all know looks
can be deceptive.' His half-closed eyes smouldered dangerously. 'What sort of an example is it to your kid sister?
Don't you have any sense of responsibility at all?'

Kid sister! Responsibility! Kelly could have hit him.

'My sister is perfectly capable of looking after herself,
and she's nineteen, nearly twenty—not seventeen.'

'And in your book that's adult?'

'Yes.'

He almost laughed. 'You don't know the meaning of
the word, Jayne. But you will by the time you leave this
country, believe me.'

There was something dreadful in his voice that made
Kelly go cold all over. 'Then it's just as well I learn
quickly,' she quipped, 'because I'm only going to be here
for three weeks.'

He looked genuinely surprised. 'But didn't Glenda tell
you?'

Kelly stared back at him. 'Tell me what?'

He put his empty plate on the coffee table before
replying; as if he enjoyed prolonging the agony, which
he probably did.

'I told her that I'd find you some work.'

'Work?' Kelly was so stunned she couldn't say anything else. 'That's absolutely out of the question,' she stammered, after a few moments. Work in America? Why hadn't Glenda said? She would never have agreed to come . . . And then the panic subsided. He couldn't *make* her do anything. Of course she wasn't going to work in this country—she was going back home to continue her degree course, and there was nothing he could do about it. Or was there? Was Joshua Brett capable of using force? *'You will go where I say—do as I say—and see only those whom I permit.'* That's what he had said on the way from the airport; and no, he hadn't been joking.

Kelly was out of her seat and halfway to the door before he caught her.

'What's the matter, Jayne? Frightened of work? Doesn't the idea appeal to you?' Long fingers curled around her arm, it didn't hurt unless she struggled, but she was struggling right now.

'Take your hands off! I'm going to get out of here. I'll—I'll go down to Florida—by bus,' she added, before he could remind her that she didn't have the fare.

His face seared with anger. 'I'll lock you in, Jayne, if I have to, believe me. It's what your father should have done years ago, if he'd had any idea.'

'But he was too busy with his new wife, wasn't he?' she screamed, suddenly not knowing whether it was herself or Jayne who was supposed to be talking. 'I've lived my own life since then and no one's going to dictate to me now!' She fought with him, beating against his chest, getting caught up with those long legs that wound between her own. He was so big and strong and her senses were filled with the intoxicating mixtures of male scent . . .

He was shaking her and the topknot came undone. 'Stop it, Jayne, for heaven's sake, this is no time to get hysterical.' But that only made it worse.

'I'm not hysterical! You don't know what my life's

been like—you don't know anything about me—and until you do you've got no right . . .'

'I've got every right,' he snarled back at her. There was hair all over her face now as he stared down at her bright, incensed features. She was breathing heavily, colour flushed her pale cheeks and brought an unknowing wantonness to her eyes. He pushed her away. 'Go to bed,' he said raggedly. 'I'll deal with you in the morning.'

'I *won't* be dismissed like a child!' Kelly stormed at his broad back.

He spun round at her. 'I *said* get to bed.'

Kelly took one more look at him—then fled.

She undressed slowly, because it was still only half past nine and she ought to stay awake for another hour at least. Not that she would ever sleep under the same roof as that wretched man.

She patrolled the bedroom in various states of undress, almost oblivious of her luxurious surroundings, but not quite. The whole house was a symphony in white, furnished to please the eye and offer no hostility. But the theory wasn't working on Kelly right now. She was fighting mad—for Jayne's sake as well as her own.

Who did Joshua Brett think he was to speak to her like that? Who was he to pass judgment on Jayne when he didn't even know her? Did he really think that Jayne launched herself into these affairs on purpose?

Kelly was completely naked now as she marched into the adjoining bathroom preparing to have another quick shower. But that would only take a few minutes and she still wanted to kill some time, so she ran a bath instead and selected some oil from the expensive display on a glass shelf. Then she grabbed the book which she had tried to read on the plane, and sank down into the scented water. Damn—the radio was still on in the bedroom. But she was too weary to get out again now. She turned a few pages, but kept seeing her sister's wretched face instead.

She sighed angrily. If Joshua Brett had seen the state Jayne had been in when her affairs went wrong . . . If he had any idea what it was like to be alone in London trying to fit into the theatre scene . . . Kelly yawned and tried to find her place again. It was time Joshua Brett was taught a lesson. It was perfectly obvious that he had never heard of, let alone suffered from, unrequited love.

She put down her book and sank back against the foam headrest. The warm oily water drifted up between her breasts and emphasised the remains of last summer's suntan. She couldn't imagine Joshua Brett knowing the meaning of love. He was a hard-headed businessman who would never understand a person's weakness. Her eyelids closed and she opened them quickly. Where was the book? She really must finish that chapter . . .

The peace was suddenly shattered. There was someone in the room and they were trying to push her under the water. She screamed and fought back. It was so cold . . .

'Stop it, you little fool!' It was Joshua, and he wanted to drown her. Then she wasn't in the bath any more, but being dragged out of it. His hands hurt under her armpits, she was kicking water everywhere. She screamed again as he banged her knee against the side of the bath.

'You were asleep,' he told her, dodging a blow. 'You could have drowned.'

Kelly stumbled against him, still dazed and silly. She was shivering, the water was stone cold . . .

'I wasn't asleep,' she muttered angrily. 'I'd just closed my eyes.'

'That's what it looked like.' He reached for one of the towels and threw it at her. 'Often read under water, do you?' and he bent down and retrieved her book that was sitting happily on the bottom. Drat!

Kelly wound the towel hastily around herself. 'What were you doing here anyway?' she grated.

'I came to ask you to turn down your radio.' He tossed the ruined book into the basin; luckily the sociological development of Third World nations didn't make any impression on him. She tried to think of an excuse

why Jayne should be reading it as Joshua reached for
another towel to dry his own hands. As he did so her
own towel slipped and as she hitched it higher she certainly wasn't thinking about her book.

'What's the matter—shy?' He laughed softly and the
rich timbre of his voice stirred something unnamed in
her soul. Only now was she beginning to realise what
had happened.

Her heart began hammering in her throat, which restricted her to silence. He laughed again, the angry dark
eyes suddenly smouldering and wicked. The space where
her knees should have been suddenly turned to cotton
wool.

'Girls like you ought to be locked up!' Then his eyes
went cold again with obvious distaste. Why? Just because she was standing here with practically nothing on!

'You're the one who barged in here—it's you who
should be locked up,' she heard herself say. 'I didn't
invite you—don't blame me for being . . .'

'Physically attractive?' he said for her.

She swallowed. 'If that's what you think.'

'Oh, I do, Jayne, I do.' There was a dreadful pulsating
silence when they just stared at each other, then his face
hardened again. 'Make sure you don't fall asleep in the
bath again.' He had his hand on the doorknob—Kelly
should have let him go.

'Next time I bathe I'll make sure the door is locked,'
some devil made her say instead.

He winced. 'Don't fight me, Jayne. I'm not a patient
man.'

'And don't you come into my room on some feeble
excuse. I've met men like you—you're only after one
thing!'

'Which you're more than willing to give.' His face
went white with anger and his hands whipped out to grab
her bare shoulders. 'If you play those games with me
you'll get hurt,' he snarled, shaking her roughly.

'You fiend!' She hit out against him, but he only
laughed at her struggles. And then Kelly went hot all
over as the towel fell to the floor. His eyes were every-

where . . . and she pushed against him, desperate now.
Desperate to get him out of here before something
dreadful happened.

And then it was over. Joshua stood back from her,
his eyes brilliant slits covered with thick lashes. His
breathing was a little faster than before, and the strong
shape of his face was slightly softened with self-satisfac-
tion. His gaze still lingered over every line and curve of
her body. She didn't have the strength to retrieve the
towel, and he had no intention of helping her.

'I wondered what I was going to do with you once I
got you here,' he purred. 'Maybe I'm beginning to get
an idea.'

'Then you can forget it,' she retorted, 'because I don't
happen to like you.'

'Of course you don't. What has *liking* got to do with
it?' And at last he picked up the towel and slowly draped
it around her shoulders, which did no good at all. 'My,
my, I believe you're blushing,' he drawled, eventually
raising his eyes to her face. 'That must be a very handy
trick for an actress. How do you manage it, exactly?'

'Get out—go on, I've had enough of you!' It hardly
seemed to matter any more, but Kelly snatched the towel
from her shoulders and whipped it tightly around herself. Joshua was still standing in the bedroom doorway.
Behind him she could see the large double bed.

For a fleeting moment she had a vision of herself as if
she had really been Jayne. Jayne would have been in
there by now, wouldn't she? Joshua was an experienced
man—virile—exciting. She could picture the two of
them between the silky sheets . . . With a supreme effort
Kelly blacked out her mind.

'I said, get out—go on!' She picked up a bar of soap
and threw it at him.

He seemed amused, not in the least put out. Which
just went to prove that he hadn't been in the least bit
affected . . .

When Kelly opened her eyes the next morning a pale
grey light was filtering between the curtains. She moaned
and stretched luxuriously, knowing there was no im-

mediate need to get up. But, despite her long hectic day yesterday, she was curiously wide awake, and she rolled over on to her back and stared up at the ceiling.

She felt restless and began fidgeting about, aware that her body ached in a curious way; a sort of unsatisfied niggle. Then slowly she began to remember her violent dream. Joshua Brett had made love to her. And what was even more amazing—she had made love to him. She could still feel his body's smooth hardness—as if his dark shadow had truly enveloped her . . .

Cross with herself, Kelly threw back the bedclothes and marched into the bathroom. She locked the door this time, then stood in the bath and gave herself a cool, refreshing shower. Dreams were strange things, she told herself severely. They didn't mean anything—usually just the opposite, in fact. She had never made love to anyone in reality, so how could she have imagined it to be all so crystal clear? . . . Then her sense of humour took over and she gave a little giggle. Surely it had been the best fantasy dream ever! What a good thing Joshua Brett would never know.

But by the time Kelly had dressed in a soft, amber-coloured skirt and creamy lacy sweater, and when her hair was piled up in a Jayne-type topknot and she had put on her face, she realised that the situation wasn't one little bit funny at all. If it had really been Jayne sitting here staring into the mirror, maybe last night's dream would have been a startling reality. Would Jayne have pushed Joshua away when the towel had fallen, and when he had looked at her with those smouldering eyes?

Kelly swallowed and purposely shut her mind to it. Joshua Brett was a dangerous man. Dangerous and ruthless and utterly without principle. If this was his idea of helping her sister it was a good thing it was Kelly who had come! But she must be careful. There was Glenda's loan to think about. She was here in Washington because she was supposed to keep Joshua Brett happy. She stared at her reflection grimly. Oh no, not that—not to save the entire Osborn fortune! Next

month she returned to university, come what might. She
had her career to think about. Nothing was going to
interfere with that. Not even Glenda's beauty-farm—
not even Jayne's continuing love-life—not even if she
had met the most unbelievable man on earth . . .

Impatiently, she scraped back her stool and went over
to the window. She pulled back the curtain and was
delighted to discover that it had been snowing. Only
lightly, just enough to powder the lawn and dust the
trees. But it reminded her that it would soon be
Christmas—and then her ready sparkle of enthusiasm
faded and died. She thought of Jayne away in the Indian
Ocean with her boy-friend, and then of Glenda in
Florida with her mountain of boy-friends . . . And Kelly
was here, in Washington, all alone. Did Joshua Brett
have someone special, instead of, or as well as, Glenda?
She wondered why the thought had never occurred to
her before.

As Kelly crept downstairs she heard breakfast-making
noises coming from the kitchen. Only then did she
realise how hungry she was. Of course, her stomach was
still on home-time and it was probably wondering when
on earth she was going to have lunch.

'Oh, I thought it was William,' she said, hesitating in
the doorway. Joshua was preparing what looked like a
king-size meal.

He didn't look surprised to find her up so early, and
if she had been expecting congratulations, she was disappointed. He was drinking his orange juice as he went
along, and as he raised the jug with an inclined head,
Kelly nodded.

'I presume you intend doing the sights,' he said, with
his back to her.

Kelly perched on the edge of a chair and stared at
him. He was wearing superbly cut dark trousers and an
immaculate white shirt, both of which seemed to have
been designed to accentuate his tiger-like grace and
virility.

'Are you?' he prompted sharply, and Kelly had to
drag her eyes away from those tantalisingly narrow hips.

If he only knew about that dream . . .

'Yes, of course, if it's allowed,' she said, recovering and sipping her drink. 'Er—doesn't William do that?' she asked, just for something to say. 'Or don't you usually have breakfast this early?'

'You call seven-thirty early? People start work early over here,' he said, piling the eggs, bacon and pancakes on to two plates. He brought the food over to the table and put one plate in front of her. She was about to protest that she only ever had a little toast, but then her stomach reminded her that starvation was about to set in, so she muttered something that sounded like thanks and glared across at him.

'William doesn't live in, I told you,' Joshua continued, settling himself at the opposite side of the table. 'He comes in when I need him.' His dark eyes veiled over. 'And as I don't need him while you're here he's having a long Christmas break.'

'I didn't come over here to fetch and carry for you!' Never mind Jayne, these were Kelly's own words, and she meant every one of them.

'Can you think of a better way of earning your keep for the present?' He was watching her carefully, too carefully, yet there hadn't been a trace of innuendo in his voice.

'What did your last slave die of?' It wasn't very original, but it was the best she could do on the spur of the moment.

'Overwork,' he replied promptly, and as the coffee finished filtering into the jug, he suggested that maybe she'd like to begin right now by getting them each a cup. He had finished his own orange juice, so he handed her across the empty glass as well.

Mutiny sat on her face and she glared at him across the table. 'Get your own coffee.' But such an unguarded remark was a mistake.

'I shan't ask you twice.' Joshua's voice was low and very controlled. 'You know what happens when you make me cross.' But Kelly only laughed at him.

'You don't have the time,' she began, but then her

breath froze in a strangled cry. Joshua was out of his
chair and hauling her to her feet. His fingers bit into her
arm as he half pushed, half carried her across the
kitchen.

'This is the coffee-maker,' he said, his voice a mixture
of ice and fire as he began opening a cupboard door.
'And these are the cups. I like one of these . . .' She tried
to struggle, but he kept her pinned against the counter
with a grip that was almost bionic. 'I don't take sugar—
and I like half-and-half cream.'

Her whole body seethed with suppressed hatred and
fury. How dared he treat her like this! Venom sprang
from her eyes, seeming to turn them from deep amber
to brittle gold. He was so tough and indestructible—
and he was hurting her—and there was nothing she
could do . . . A red-hot determination to get even with
him burned at her soul.

But now wasn't the time. She relaxed suddenly and
he released his hold very, very slowly indeed.

He still had a napkin in one hand, and with it he
touched his lips briefly. To hide a laugh? Hardly. The
wretched man wouldn't know how to laugh.

'I'll let you get on with it.' His voice didn't waver,
and when she clunked the coffee next to his plate she
spilt some in the saucer.

He didn't say anything, he just looked at her—and
for maybe half a minute they had an out-and-out eye
battle, until Kelly couldn't stand the strain any more,
and with an exasperated groan she took the coffee back
to the sink and wiped the saucer.

'Thank you,' he said quietly, when she returned the
cup with more care. 'You can do the same thing tomorrow morning—only next time I shall expect a smile.'

'You can go to . . .'

He raised a finger. 'Ah, ah, ah,' he said, shaking his
head. 'If you want a lift into D.C. the least you can do
is be polite.'

Kelly bounced down on her chair again in tight-lipped
silence. It was only in the Army that they could charge
you with dumb insolence, wasn't it?

CHAPTER THREE

'HAVEN'T you got a hat? It'll be cold out there.' Joshua was waiting for her at the bottom of the stairs—he was wearing the jacket of his suit now, and was about to put on a beautiful fawn camelhair coat.

'I don't wear hats,' said Kelly. Jayne didn't either, so that was all right.

He looked about to comment, then changed his mind as he gathered his briefcase from a chair. 'You might like these.' His voice was coolly indifferent as he handed her a pile of guides to the city. 'Where exactly did you want to begin?'

Kelly shrugged as she did up the buttons of her fur jacket. She was wearing her own long black leather boots and a sturdy matching shoulder bag, but Jayne's silver fox fur made her feel outrageous—even pretty. The sun was coming out now; suddenly she felt it was going to be a gorgeous day.

'How about the White House, Capitol and the Monument for starters?' she said, giving him a ravishing to-hell-with-it smile. As she did so, he paused in the act of opening the front door and something made him catch his breath. His eyes looked different, then they quickly darted away from her face. He opened the door properly this time and the icy blast hit her right between the eyes.

The long, luxurious car was deliciously warm, but as they approached Washington along the bank of the Potomac, Kelly saw that the still, shallow waters near an island were frozen. It had taken roughly half an hour to drive from Mclean, the early morning traffic had been heavy—but they hadn't been delayed. She felt a bubble of excitement as they turned left on to a bridge, its classical style making a magnificent approach to the city by way of the white marble Lincoln Memorial.

Kelly's eyes were everywhere; there was traffic everywhere, and she swivelled round in her seat to gaze at the columned portico that made the memorial look like a Grecian temple. And then Joshua was leaving the main belt of traffic and seemed to be heading for a park; at least there were grass and water and a place to stop the car. But the roar of the city was still only a stone's throw away.

'I thought you had to get to the office,' she said with some alarm as he climbed out of the car when she did. She was looking forward to a day when she could really be herself—the last thing she wanted was to trail round with Joshua Brett.

'I'm only going to show you where to go,' he said, locking the doors and throwing his briefcase into the boot. Then he locked that carefully as well, and gave the catch a good tug. For some reason the straight-forward, everyday action made Kelly suddenly realise how important his work must be. He was a British space designer working with the Americans. That meant he had to be really good. There were probably secrets in that briefcase . . . special things that had been discussed over the weekend. She turned her jacket collar up and tucked down her chin, glancing at him through a soft edge of bluey-grey fur. She remembered all those manned space flights back in the seventies—and then the equally incredible space-shuttle . . . And Joshua *understood* these things. He designed equipment to carry out these astounding feats of technology . . . It made him as far out of her reach now as when she had been a young schoolgirl of thirteen.

He held her arm as they hurried across two roads of double lane traffic. It didn't mean anything; he probably didn't want the inconvenience of her being run over. They climbed the grassy bank in silence and there, ahead of them through the bare trees, rose the fine white column of the Monument. Its needle-sharp point seemed to pierce the brilliant blue sky. It was circled by red, white and blue Union flags, all standing to attention as the bitter wind blew off the water. Kelly shivered, the tops of her ears almost hurt with the cold.

They weren't the only people sightseeing, even at this time in the morning, and as they passed a bunch of young Americans, more than one of them gave Kelly an appreciative grin.

She felt the hand on her arm tighten. Why was he still holding it, anyway? She wriggled out of his grasp and glared at him defiantly.

'I can find my way from here,' she muttered. 'There's no need for you to come any further.' They had crossed the grass now and had reached the main road. The traffic lights said 'walk', and that was what she wanted to do—just walk away from Joshua's accusing eyes. Was it her fault if men looked at her that way?

'The White House is that way, the Capitol is down there.' He said it with as much authority as if he had designed the place himself. 'I'll meet you for lunch at one.'

'No!' Kelly spoke more sharply than she had intended and he was instantly suspicious. 'There's no need,' she hurried on. 'I know you're busy—I'm perfectly capable of looking after myself, you know.'

'But is Washington equally capable, with you on the loose?' he said grimly.

Kelly fumed and almost stamped her foot. 'You don't trust me, do you?'

'No.'

'*Oh.*' This time she did stamp, her face fixed and mutinous, her eyes darting around wildly for a means of escape. 'You're not my keeper—I'll do as I like . . .'

'And how do you intend getting home, exactly?' His warm breath vaporised in the cold air—he looked like a dragon breathing fire.

But Kelly had done her homework, nothing was going to put her off. 'I'll go on the metro,' she snapped.

'It doesn't go that far—you'll have a long walk.'

'Then I'll get a bus.'

'Which one?' he retorted, as if he was giving her the third degree.

Kelly's eyes blazed. 'I do have a tongue in my head!'

'Good. Use it to find out where the Natural History

Museum is. One o'clock. Bottom floor. Members' dining room. Be there.' And with that parting shot he turned on his heel and strode away. Kelly pulled a face at him—trouble was, he didn't see.

Luckily the Monument opened at nine, which was just as well, although *he* wouldn't have worried if she had been left standing around in the freezing cold for ever. The first group of tourists was just being ushered into the lift and there was plenty of room for Kelly as she ran to join them.

The lift attendant greeted everyone warmly and gave them a short potted history of the towering structure as they sped upwards. Kelly sighed contentedly; friendly efficiency—yes, she was back in America. What a pleasant change it made from the Anglo-Saxon hostility out at Mclean.

As the lift doors opened Kelly made a big effort to push all her problems away; for a while it was easy as the grace and beauty of Washington soothed her mind.

The view from the top of the Monument was incredible. From one of the windows she could see the White House far, far below, and someone was pointing out the big Christmas tree surrounded by smaller trees that represented each State. Kelly resolved to go down afterwards and have a closer look.

From another window the grassy Mall stretched long and wide down to the shining white Capitol building at the far end. Her guide-book said that the assortment of imposing buildings on each side of the Mall were the various National Museums. She was supposed to be meeting Joshua somewhere down there. Kelly tightened her lips—he would be lucky!

She moved around to the other side and focussed her camera on the Potomac river and beyond, into Virginia. There was some sort of a lake, a tidal basin according to the book, and another round white monument—something else to investigate later. She saw where Joshua had parked the car—and the roads they had hurried across when he had held her arm. She recalled the pressure of his long fingers as easily as if he had been standing here right now. Was there to be no peace from the wretched man, ever?

The light sprinkle of overnight snow had mostly vanished as Kelly went back to ground level and began wandering around. With her hands in her pockets and her coat collar turned up, she crunched her way down the gravelly paths of the Mall, dodging joggers who looked warm and snug in track suits and ear muffs. Kelly shivered a bit and wished she had a hat. It hadn't occurred to her that it would be so much colder than back home. She would have to go inside somewhere just to keep warm. The building with the dome she was passing was the Natural History Museum—but nothing was going to get her in there. Next came the Art Gallery—that would do fine. Kelly ran up the steps and swung open the enormous, heavily studded door. Warmth—blessed warmth enveloped her. She began undoing her coat.

She did a few of the early Italian galleries, then glanced at her watch. It was eleven o'clock. Already? Eventually she found her way to the basement cafeteria, and sat watching a wall of water pouring down from the street-level fountain above. Behind the glass, the water distorted reflections so that images couldn't really be seen—except those in your mind. Kelly stirred her coffee—and imagined Joshua . . .

Joshua beneath the chestnut tree, sitting on an English lawn that fine afternoon. She had offered him a cake; he hadn't noticed, and she had just stood beside his chair watching the strong lines of his face become alive and animated as he had talked with her father. Stuart must have said something, because Joshua suddenly turned and looked up at Kelly, and although he smiled and took a cake she knew that he had hardly seen her— or tasted it. Glenda had sent her indoors then for some more hot water—and the kettle had taken ages to boil. Joshua had left soon afterwards and that had been the last time Kelly had seen him—until yesterday.

She sighed and pushed the memory away because it served no useful purpose. Everything was different now.

She was different, and Joshua was different. In fact, he
wasn't turning out to be the man she had expected at
all. Oh, there was that icy hardness she had expected
and obviously he had the worst possible opinion of her,
which didn't matter, of course, but it was irritating. Yet
there was something about him that she couldn't quite
name—something that she hadn't been prepared for.
Was it him? Or was it her own reaction to him that she
didn't quite understand? Instinct told her to keep out of
his way, yet some fatal fascination always seemed to
make her stay. Hadn't she sworn not to have lunch with
him? Yet even as she had said it some devil inside her
head had laughed, knowing she would.

Kelly's eyes roamed around the pleasant, airy cafeteria. It was beginning to get busy with the early lunchtime rush. A family arrived to share her table, their trays
piled high with open sandwiches and bowls of colourful
salad. She left them to it, assuring them that they weren't
driving her away. But she felt suddenly depressed for
the first time, trapped in a situation she had no control
over. And even outside the bright sunshine bouncing
from the white buildings did nothing much to cheer her.

Until she heard music and, following the sound, she
found a colourful skating rink tucked unexpectedly between the grand edifices of Gallery and Museum. She
sat on a low wall for a while and watched as children
and adults swirled round and round, their bright
coloured anoraks a brilliant contrast to the white ice
and vivid blue sky. It was an oasis of cheerfulness amidst
the cool, classical shapes that was Washington's centre.
Kelly suddenly was glad she had come. What did it
matter if Joshua Brett was a bit more of a problem than
she had imagined? Once Glenda had secured her loan
there was nothing to stop Kelly returning to England
... nothing except money! But she purposely decided
not to think about that!

She found herself leaving the skaters and making her
way across the grass to the next building. Bottom floor,
he had said. One o'clock. That gave her just enough
time to go and freshen up.

Kelly stared at her reflection in the mirror of the ladies' rest room. She was becoming familiar with her new look. The topknot still made her head ache a bit, but the few loose tendrils seemed to accentuate the bone structure of her face. It made her look delicate—almost ethereal. Not that Joshua would notice—or even care if he did.

She was there first, and she sat outside the restaurant, positioning herself so that he would see her from whichever way he came. She waited, holding her breath as the lift doors opened again; it was two minutes before the hour. He looked neither surprised nor pleased, and she was instantly cross with herself. She shouldn't have come—why or when had she changed her mind? She couldn't remember.

'What have you been doing?' he asked, when they had selected their meal from the help-yourself table along one side of the room. Their wine came, and Kelly paused before replying.

'Don't you mean what have I been up to?' she said, when they were alone again.

He looked at her coolly. 'If you like.'

She shrugged. 'Planning a revolution!'

'Only one?'

'There's only one of you.'

He put down his knife and fork. 'I'm not the enemy, Jayne.'

She stared at him. 'You can sit there and say that after last night's little fiasco?' She was a fool to remind him, but somehow the words had just tumbled out.

Now it was his turn to shrug. 'Habit,' he said indifferently, and she could have hit him. 'Usually—when there's a naked woman in my bathroom . . .'

'It wasn't your bathroom!'

His dark eyes widened. 'So who's counting?' Then his slow gaze lowered to what he could see of her above the table. He seemed to look away with reluctance, but as he did so that cold, hard look came back to his face. 'It won't happen again, believe me,' he said eventually. 'The last thing I want is a little out-of-work actress hanging round my neck.' She felt as if she had been slapped in the face. 'Is that what you expected, Jayne? Is that why you came? Did you think I would make a convenient meal-ticket for the next few months, until you launched yourself into another wild affair?'

Kelly dragged her chair back. 'I'm not staying to be insulted!' But he caught her arm and pulled her down again.

'Don't make a scene.' His fingers hurt like hell—it was a wonder she didn't scream. 'Be thankful I'm not tempted——'

'Aren't you?' she interrupted fiercely.

The muscles down his face flexed. 'Not any more. You're too young for me, Jayne. And I'm certainly too old for you.'

'You mean you couldn't keep pace?' Her voice was loaded with sarcasm.

Anger seared his face and a wild, dangerous look glistened behind his eyes. 'I ought to . . .' He breathed raggedly, then changed his mind and gave a low, steadying sigh. Kelly was trembling; for a second she had unleashed something deep within him. But it had gone again—icy hostility was back.

'If you want to be treated like an adult, it's about time you started acting like one.'

Somehow Kelly managed to laugh. Jayne not an adult! That was a joke.

'Maturity isn't a question of climbing into a man's bed,' he said, staring at the pulse beating against her throat. 'In fact, sometimes it's just the opposite. When I was your age . . .'

'You'd just begun working for my father and you were the brightest light in the design team that he'd ever seen,' she recounted theatrically.

He looked surprised. 'You were only twelve—you remember?'

Wrong. She had been only nine and she would never forget. 'But we can't all have Master's degrees and be brilliant,' she said instead.

'Heaven forbid! But that doesn't give you the excuse to waste your life.'

'I see. So if we're not academic or productive it's a waste, is it? Well, I don't see life like that. Progress, technology—that's great—but let's leave it to people like you.' She nearly said '*cold-blooded* people like you', but somehow managed to stop herself. 'But there's more to our existence that having the things we *need*. Do we *need* music? Do we *need* flowers? But can you imagine what life would be like without them?'

Joshua wiped his lips with a napkin and took a long drink of wine. Then he looked at her, and it was quite impossible to tell what he was thinking. 'And where do you fit in?' he asked at last.

Kelly played for time; it was getting difficult trying to remember that she was supposed to be Jayne.

'People need entertaining . . .'

'After a hard day at the salt mines?'

They laughed together involuntarily, until they both remembered the situation, and looked away.

'Something like that,' said Kelly, staring down at her plate.

'But you're not, are you?' he said, and his face and voice were back to normal. 'Entertaining, I mean. I told you yesterday, six months' work in the past four years—and I think I was being generous.'

'It isn't easy trying to find that sort of job.'

'Then I suggest you change your profession—or economise.'

Kelly had finished her roast beef and she put her knife and fork together with a clatter. 'I'm going to have to, aren't I, now that you've got this new arrangement with Glenda.'

Joshua refused to be drawn on that subject. 'What are your plans? When you go back?'

'So you are letting me go back,' she said quickly, 'even though you only sent me a one-way ticket.'

'If you earn the fare. Why so surprised? It's what most people do, Jayne, work for their living. So,' he shrugged, 'if you want to get back to England—' he lowered his voice menacingly, and left the rest unsaid.

'I have no intention of working in this country——'
she began.

'And I have every intention that you shall.' The waitress cleared their plates. 'Coffee?' he asked her automatically.

'Please. But I'd like a piece of that chocolate thing
first.' Just because he didn't eat pudding it didn't mean
that she was going to do without.

'I thought actresses were always watching their
figures,' he said with a supercilious air.

'But I'm not an actress, am I?' she retorted, without
thinking, and when he looked surprised, she added,
'Unless you count six months in four years.'

His lips twitched, but she didn't stay to hear what he
said. The display of desserts down the end of the long
table looked absolutely delicious. As she returned to her
seat she was aware of more than one pair of eyes upon
her. Sometimes it was nice being dressed up to look like
Jayne. And then she realised that all the other people
thought she was herself. What would Joshua think of
her if he knew who she really was? For a moment it was
difficult not to giggle.

She was a long time eating her chocolate pie so that
he had to wait for his coffee. When the coffee eventually
came, he drank his black. Yuk! thought Kelly, he
would.

'I suppose, just by chance, you don't happen to have
any work arranged for the New Year?' he asked, looking
at her over the top of his cup.

Kelly knew what was coming next and for a moment
she was tempted to invent a super part in a West End
play. But she rejected the idea almost immediately.
Joshua could easily check that . . . 'I've got one or two
auditions lined up,' she muttered instead.

'When?'

'At the beginning of January.'

'Is there any chance that you'll get either of the parts?'
Joshua asked, forcing her to concentrate on the lie.
Heavens, why had she begun it?

She looked down at her own cup. 'I'm not sure—I can only try.'

He didn't believe her. She *knew* he didn't believe her. She could feel those shrewd eyes bringing the flame to her cheeks.

'Do you still have the same agent?' he asked after several agonising moments.

Agent! Lord, was he going to phone him? Did he know Jayne's agent? 'No, no, I changed about a year ago.'

'You're lying.' His lips compressed into a tight line. 'You have no auditions arranged. It's just an excuse to get back to London.'

'What if it is? What's wrong with that?'

'Everything.' He finished his coffee and signalled to the waitress for the bill. 'But it won't work, Jayne. You're not going back to London. You're going to stay here and start earning your living.'

'You've got to be joking!' Kelly clattered her cup down in the saucer, aware that several people at the other tables had turned her way. 'It's absolutely out of the question,' she said in a lower voice, 'and anyway, you can't *force* me . . .'

'Can't I?'

She thought of Glenda who was desperate for Joshua's loan, and Jayne who would be desperate if the London flat was sold. 'That's blackmail,' she said, and he knew exactly what she meant.

'If you choose to see it that way . . .' he trailed off as he was given the bill and slowly pushed back his chair. 'And you can begin tomorrow morning,' he added calmly, 'at seven-thirty. I like my breakfast prompt.'

They were back upstairs in the large, echoing entrance foyer before Kelly could trust herself to speak. 'There's a law against slavery,' she said, glaring at the giant stuffed elephant and wishing for a moment that it would come to life and trample Joshua Brett to death.

'And there ought to be a law against the things you've been up to,' he responded smartly, as they began putting on their coats before braving the sub-zero temperature outside. She was still fumbling with her gloves and he seemed to be waiting for her. That was the last thing she wanted right now.

'You go on—I'm not in a hurry,' she said angrily, because what else was there to say to such a wretched man who always insisted in having the last word.

'I'm going back to Mclean with you,' he said, as if she was daft not to have realised it. 'I've just closed the office for Christmas. It's only four days away,' he added, pushing open the heavy entrance doors.

The cold hit her and she almost gasped. 'That's a long time off,' she said nastily, making it sound as if she was surprised at his generosity to the staff.

He chose to take her words at their face value. 'Most of them are British—they've gone back to their families in the U.K.'

'Why didn't you?' Didn't he have a home in Gloucestershire? Once again she realised there was very little she knew about this cold, remote man.

'This year I chose to stay here. There's quite a party scene at this time of the year. In fact, we've been invited out to one tonight.'

Kelly nearly fell down the rest of the steps. Going out to a party with Joshua Brett! But then she realised that it wouldn't be like that. She would be the recalcitrant little nuisance dragged along because he wanted to keep his eye on her.

'Anyone I know?' she asked automatically, having a vague idea that some of her stepmother's friends lived in Washington.

He shook his head. 'Glenda hasn't met them. He works at the British Embassy . . . By the way, they've got carol singing there this afternoon. Would you like to go?'

Kelly felt suddenly happy, but couldn't say why. 'That sounds really Christmassy—great!' Joshua looked surprised and she realised she had made a bit of a mistake. Carol singing wasn't exactly Jayne's idea of fun. Still, he didn't know her well enough to realise that. But she shrugged and tried to sound less enthusiastic. 'At least it'll be something exciting to put on the postcards home.'

Home! Kelly! The poor kid sister left alone for Christmas. Joshua's brows creased, she saw the next question forming in his mind and it spelt trouble. Where was Kelly? Who was she spending Christmas with? More bending the truth—and Kelly was getting fed up with it.

But luckily they had to cross a busy road and by the time they reached the other side, he seemed to have forgotten all about it. After a few more moments Kelly began breathing more easily again.

They walked back down the Mall over long shadows cast by the winter sun as it began its slow descent behind the trees. The air was sharp and brittle and the towering white Monument looked so cold that if you touched it your fingers would be frostbitten.

Joshua took her arm, simply because she wasn't walking quickly enough, and they both watched as a slow, low-flying airliner passed behind the Monument on its way down the Potomac river towards the city's busy airport. For the first time Kelly noticed clouds in the western sky. It looked like snow.

It was four o'clock when they got back to Mclean. There was no sign of William. Had Joshua really sent him away for the holidays?

'We don't need to leave again for an hour,' he told her, throwing his briefcase on the hall chair and shrugging himself out of his coat. 'I'd like a cup of tea, please, Jayne. In the sitting room. I'll go and light the fire.'

She stared after him, her hands halfway out of her gloves. Tea, was it? He had a hope! She ran up the stairs to her room—decided it wasn't the safest place—and ran back downstairs again. Okay, Jayne would make the tea and Jayne would be all smiles—for the moment. Jayne would even go to the carol-singing, she was quite looking forward to that ... But afterwards, when it came to the party—well, *Kelly* was beginning to have a little scheme for that!

The carol-singing, he had told her, was taking place in the British Embassy Rotunda, which turned out to be a circular, modern, glassy-looking structure extending from one corner of the building. It was already crowded when Joshua and Kelly arrived, and although he nodded to several people in the distance, there was no opportunity to find his particular friends.

Kelly was given some music, they were already about to begin, and it seemed strange, yet comforting, to be standing singing *Once in Royal David's City* with a crowd of expatriate Britons and their friends. There was a choir in the gallery, and high above everyone, looking splendid in the light, modern building, hung beautiful banners embroidered in rich and brilliant colours. They looked new. Kelly wondered who had made them.

Joshua's voice rose deep and strong above her head. He was a rich bass-baritone, but she had the impression that he was holding back, so that he shouldn't outshine the weaker voices all around him. The carol ended, and then they all launched into *The Holly and the Ivy* which was one of Kelly's favourites, and for a while she forgot all about her problems and let a blissful, Christmassy feeling seep into her bones. After all, wasn't it supposed to be the season of goodwill?

When they all stopped singing it had obviously been decided to give the choir a rest and a man began reading an extract from Dickens' *A Christmas Carol*. Some latecomers arrived halfway through and Joshua closed up the gap that had been between him and Kelly; in the squeeze his body brushed lightly against her; Scrooge was forgotten—her whole back tingled.

There were mince pies and mulled wine afterwards, and the crush in the small reception area was terrific.

'I'm so glad you could come . . .' a woman's voice began behind them.

'We only just made it in time,' Joshua replied. He was smiling. So these were his friends. For a moment it seemed strange to Kelly that he should have a life beyond the existence she had created for him. 'Jayne Osborn—she's over for Christmas.' He might have been introducing a business colleague whom he had just met. 'This is Peter and Jean Rawlings, whose party we've been invited to tonight.'

The preliminaries over, Jean Rawlings launched into the usual social chat. How delighted she was that Kelly could come. Had Kelly visited America before? She was a pleasant attractive woman somewhere in her forties. Kelly took an instant liking to her and returned the questions with a pile of her own. How long had the Rawlings been out here? Were they enjoying Washington? . . . Out of the corner of her ear she could hear Peter Rawlings and Joshua discussing the state of the dollar against the pound.

They were joined by more friends, and the introductions began again. If anyone wondered at her exact relationship with Joshua, they were all too diplomatic to let it show. Somehow Kelly found herself drifting with the women towards the plates of hot mince pies. 'I really shouldn't,' came the usual cry from someone, but of course they all did, and Kelly laughed and turned round to see where Joshua was—and the sight of him caused a curious sensation deep inside; it was a cross between sickness and physical pain. The mince pie turned to cotton-wool in her mouth, and she coughed and turned back to the women, and hoped that no one had noticed.

Joshua hadn't been in the crowd with the rest of the men. He had drawn a little apart, near where everyone's coats had been piled on a table, and he was talking to a ravishing brunette—well, if talking was the word . . . His head had been bending towards her slightly, as if he didn't want to miss a single word she had said. That was all. That was all she had given herself time to see. But it was enough. The pain had gone now and the sickness was reduced to a queasy feeling in the pit of her stomach.

What a strange thing to happen. Kelly was puzzled. What on earth did it mean?

A little voice in her head said, 'You've fallen in love with him', but she refused to listen to such a silly idea.

CHAPTER FOUR

THEY drove home in silence. It was snowing in the car's headlights and Kelly stared at the lights of Washington from the other side of the river, but she didn't really see their beauty. She was still back at the Rotunda; the girl had vanished into the crowd, and Joshua hadn't mentioned her. That meant she must have been important. Then the road turned away from the Potomac and climbed up between the trees, so she stared at the snow instead. It didn't seem to be settling.

Joshua switched the radio on and flicked through chat-shows and news broadcasts until he found a station which was transmitting dramatic, orchestral music; Wagner's *Tristan und Isolde*, unless she was very much mistaken. She watched his hand as he depressed the buttons. There was something about him now, some inner coil of tension. The car bristled with it, like static electricity rustling through a petticoat. She was aware of him in a way that she had never been aware of anyone before. If he moved, she felt a similar response in her own limbs. If he was cross, she felt apprehensive. He drove with a heavy, brooding silence that dampened her own spirits as well. He was thinking of the girl he had met—she was obviously more than a friend ... The music rose to a rich, powerful climax, the quadraphonic sound filling the car with passion and death ... But he abruptly switched it off just as it reached the piercingly sweet bit. The man had no soul. Kelly could have hit him.

The house welcomed them back with soft porch lights and its Christmas evergreen wreath. Some of the houses had extravagant displays of seasonal paraphernalia, but Kelly liked the simple wreaths best—or the houses where they just had a single candle in each window.

There was still no sign of William, and as they shed

their coats in the hall, she decided she was going to ask.

'I told you—he's off for the holidays.' Joshua switched on lights as he made his way to the kitchen. His years of working mostly in America hadn't changed his desire for a good old British 'cuppa'.

Kelly was right behind him.

'Perhaps you can tell me what exactly is going to happen?'

'Now—or in the future?' he asked, with a strange sort of distant look in his eyes.

'Both.' Her reaction to the brunette was beginning to annoy Kelly. If there was another woman in his life—someone he was serious about—then she wanted to know right now!

He filled the kettle, then leaned back against the sink. 'About *now* I'd say you were going to make me a pot of tea—and the future,' he shrugged as if it didn't matter, 'that, my dear Jayne, is an unwritten book.'

She wasn't his dear Jayne—she was Kelly. She pushed the irrational thought away.

'If William isn't here what are we going to do about Christmas?'

'We're going to work.'

'Work?' Surely even he didn't resort to that. 'I thought you said your office was closed.'

The kettle began to sing—he ignored it. 'You don't imagine I'd let you anywhere near my office,' he said superiorly. 'There's more than one kind of work.'

'And I'm not slaving over a stove and cooking your Christmas dinner, if that's what you think. Is that why you invited me over—to get cheap labour for the holidays?'

'Who said anything about slaving over a hot stove? Where you're going it'll be a bit colder than that.' He was enjoying himself. The kettle boiled then switched itself off automatically.

'What in heaven's name do you mean?'

'If you bring that tea into the study I'll show you,' and he left Kelly banging about the kitchen in an exasperated temper. She found the tray and the special cups he liked. But he needn't think he had won. She was only doing it because the mince pies and mulled wine had made her dry.

When she carried it all through to the study he had cleared a place for the tray on the corner of his desk. It was a large room, more like a library really. Books lined three walls between windows that looked out on to a dark wood. Joshua was closing the curtains when she came in—for some reason she felt suddenly trapped.

'Have a look at these,' he said, dumping a pile of books and papers on a leather-covered settee. This room wasn't all cool and white and gold; it was brown and green, heavy, chunky, earthy colours. Kelly had the feeling that the rest of the house belonged to Washington, but that this room belonged to him. The central heating kept the whole house warm twenty-four hours a day, but there was a log fire in here as well, yet he didn't light it. Probably because they would be going out again soon.

She took her tea to a side table and curled up in a corner of the settee. Joshua wasn't watching her, he had become engrossed in some paperwork that he had fished out of his briefcase. She lowered her eyes at last and saw that he had given her lots of books on birds.

'What's this supposed to tell me?' she said after a while.

'What to look for.' And when even he realised this was hardly an explanation, he put down his pen and came over to join her on the settee. 'You can see that one here,' he said, pointing to a beautiful red bird on the page that was open. It was a cardinal, and looked exotic enough to have been in a South American jungle.

'You mean now—in winter?'

He nodded. 'I think even you could recognise that.'

She glared at him. 'Why should I have to?'

'Because that's what you'll be doing over Christmas.'

'What *I'll* be doing?'

'Okay,' he shrugged, 'what we'll both be doing.'

'Climbing over garden fences looking for—for Cardinals?' It was too absurd for words.

'Not quite.' He didn't smile. 'We're going to the Blue
Ridge Mountains to count birds—all the birds—well, as
many as we can see.' He said it in the tone of voice he
might have used to announce that he was going to the
shops to buy a quarter of a pound of tea!

'You're mad!'

He gave her a long, enigmatic look. 'Very probably.'
Then he went back to the desk and poured himself another cup of tea.

Kelly's mind refused to operate. Going to the Blue
Ridge Mountains to count birds! Where were the Blue
Ridge Mountains anyway? No one in their right mind
traipsed off to the middle of nowhere at Christmas.
What about the brunette at the Embassy? What would
she have to say?

He was joking.

A man like Joshua Brett wouldn't joke.

She would stay here in Mclean—he couldn't make
her go with him ...

Joshua Brett could make *anyone* do *anything*.

She turned the pages of the book. Ruffed Grouse,
Bobwhite, Yellow-Shafted Flicker ... birds she had
never heard of before. Her eyelids grew heavy, it had
been such a long day yesterday—as she fell asleep she
realised she was suffering from jet-lag.

'Jayne.' A deep voice was speaking softly and
someone was touching her arm. *Jayne?* What was she
doing here? Kelly struggled to open her eyes—and then
she remembered. Joshua was bending over her, a large
mug of coffee in one hand.

She had been lying out flat on the settee— there was a
rug thrown over her ... 'What's the time?' she asked
sleepily, remembering the party.

'Nearly nine o'clock,' and he smiled briefly when he
saw her distress. 'It doesn't matter if we're late. We don't
have far to go.'

Her topknot was coming undone and thick dark hair
tumbled across her face as she struggled to sit up. She
could feel his eyes watching her as she tugged at the
elastic band and gave her head a shake. The freedom

and movement of her hair was an almost sensual pleasure after its tight constriction. She opened her eyes again and caught an unusual look on Joshua's face; he was angry—but this time he looked angry with himself.

She sipped her coffee, still trying to blink her eyes awake, and he went and stood with his back to the unlit fire. His feet were a little apart, and she could sense a certain tension in his body, like an athlete ready to spring. He was watching every move she made, she could feel those dark, disturbing eyes on her hair, her hands, her body . . .

'You can be ready in an hour?' His voice was tight.

'Of course.' She stared up at him through a veil of hair, then wound some of it behind her ear. He looked thoughtful for a second and she imagined he was going to say something. But he didn't—and almost immediately the strange feeling passed away.

'I'll go and get changed myself,' he said, tidying up a sheaf of papers that were spread over his desk. The tea tray had gone, he looked as if he had been working there for some time. It seemed strange to think that he had been doing so while she had slept here—so close to him . . .

'What sort of a party will it be?' she asked, her eyes on his strong, well-groomed hands under the light from the table lamp.

'Dinner jacket—formal,' he replied, and Kelly nodded, pleased with herself, because that suited her little plan.

She didn't rush, and when Joshua left her she sat on in the study slowly finishing her coffee, and mentally going through her wardrobe, trying to decide what to wear. The idea had come to her at lunchtime, when he had gone on and on calling her Jayne. If it was Jayne he wanted, then it was Jayne she would be. Which meant the red dress—or maybe the peacock-blue . . . She was still tired and it took all her resolution to drag herself from the settee, but once she had showered and spread the dresses out on the bed, she was beginning to look forward to the party—or at least, Jayne was!

Kelly tried on the red dress first, and stared at her reflection in open-mouthed wonder. Wow! Was that really her? Scarlet silk clung to her everywhere—except all those parts which were decidedly bare! She swirled her hair up on top of her head, and pouted seductively. Great—let the brunette compete with that! Only ... well, maybe it was a bit much. So she peeled it off and climbed into the peacock-blue. The long skirt folded over on the floor, so she slipped on her spiky sandals and the length was just right. She twirled around getting the feel of the dress. That was better—it was low enough and revealing enough, but not quite as sensational as the red affair. After all, this was the first party—it might be a good idea to keep the mind-blowing dress in reserve!

She piled her hair up—then decided on a compromise by leaving the back hanging down in a thick coil, rather like a girl she had seen on a Greek vase painting. Then she selected a thin gold bracelet and a similar chain for her neck. These were pieces of her own jewellery, she was used to them, they were comfortable and familiar. But as she gathered her fur jacket and a little evening bag, she realised that perhaps she was more like Jayne than she had imagined. The dress fitted. The colour suited her. Okay, so maybe she wouldn't have chosen this dress, but that was because she didn't usually attend these kind of functions. A student didn't have much time to get beyond the local folk festival, or maybe a provincial concert. But if she had moved in Jayne's circle wasn't this the sort of thing she would wear?

She turned out the light in her room and slowly wandered downstairs. Maybe she didn't want to be Jayne tonight, after all. Maybe she just wanted to be Kelly. Would Joshua notice the difference? Come to that, what difference would there be?

He was waiting in the drawing room, a drink in one hand while he idly turned the pages of a Natural History magazine. The table lamp beside his chair was the only illumination in the room, it made a white pool of light which accentuated the deep blackness of his jacket. For a second their eyes met and there was a fire—a spark of mutual attraction—Kelly's heart pounded and a twisting sensation seared her stomach. Then he stood up and put the magazine on the coffee table—when he looked at her again the magic had gone.

He brought the car around to the front. The porch steps were dry, but beyond them the snow was beginning to settle. Joshua leaned across and opened her door and she ran down and climbed into the car as fast as her spiky sandals would let her.

'Did you make sure the front door was locked?'

'Yes.' She glanced at him sideways as he slowly edged the car towards the road. Physical attraction, that was what he had momentarily felt for her when she had walked into the room. But there was some cold, inner strength about him that told her physical attraction wouldn't be enough. He wouldn't have an affair with a woman unless he liked her personally, as well. And with all Washington to choose from he was hardly likely to be hard up! An *affair*! Heavens, what was she *thinking* of!

Kelly nestled back in the luxurious upholstery of the big car, as Joshua held the powerful engine in check. They slowly purred around the fashionable suburbs; lights twinkled from houses set back between the trees. Kelly closed her eyes and wished the journey could go on for ever. Instinct told her that this was as close to Joshua as she would ever be.

It was a glittering, bright-lights party that extended to every corner of the house. The drinks and an incredible array of refreshments were set out downstairs in what the Americans called their 'rec-room'. Normally it housed the family's ping-pong table and one of their son's stereo gear, but all that had been swept aside and now there were soft lights and soft music, bright chatter, and a colourful mixture of accents and dresses. People had spread upstairs as well; there was a beautiful drawing room with a huge log fire, and another smaller sitting room, where older guests were already engaged in cosy, restful conversation. The house was filled with plants,

there were beautiful poinsettias everywhere. Jean
Rawlings came up to greet them, and Joshua was full of
apologies for being late.

'Jayne was jet-lagged,' he explained, giving their host-
ess one of his ravishing smiles.

'Of course she was—such a bore, isn't it?' She smiled
at Kelly and the younger girl knew she didn't believe a
word of it.

She glanced at Joshua, expecting him to be cross, but
instead he looked perfectly wicked. Did he often turn
up late for parties? Surely all his girl-friends weren't jet-
lagged! And then for the next hour and a half she discovered another Joshua; the one who talked with women
and left a certain light sparkling in their eyes. He did it
with a pink-tinted woman over fifty and with gawky
schoolgirls nearer fifteen. But there were a lot of women
nearer his own age, and they all talked and laughed and
flirted with him outrageously, and the dark, smouldering
eyes were more than willing to reply.

In the end, Kelly got fed up with seeing him have
such a super time, so she wandered upstairs where the
young set had gathered, and pretty soon she was drawn
into their circle.

They were interested to hear all about her, yet for
once Kelly was typically English and extremely reticent.
She felt uncomfortable posing as Jayne, so she just stuck
to a few basic facts that could have applied to either
sister.

One of the unattached men, a good-looking American
in his late twenties, eventually separated her from the
group and found a cosy nook beside the log fire. He
fetched her a drink, introduced himself as Russ, then
tried to pick her up in the most charming way possible.
What a change to be cosseted and flirted with. Kelly
settled down to enjoy herself—and flirted back.

All went well, and she was almost able to forget about
Joshua, until nearly midnight. Then, when a group of
people moved away from the fire, Kelly could see right
through an archway to the hall, and the girl was there—
the brunette from the Embassy. She was wearing a coat,

as if she had just arrived. There was no sign of Joshua, but Kelly knew she wouldn't have to wait long. Right. By the time the girl had got rid of her coat he was there.

They were beginning to serve coffee; waiters with silver coffee pots moved silently between the guests. In a moment Joshua would turn round and see Kelly, and it was suddenly important that if he had someone else, then so should she. The American made a joke, and Kelly automatically laughed. 'Yes, I'm a Snoopy fan too,' and at that precise moment Joshua looked over his shoulder and saw her.

He was angry, and for a second their eyes met in open hostility. Kelly glared back at him. He had the women, so why shouldn't Kelly have this man? She touched Russ's arm and smiled up at him dazzlingly.

'Say, maybe we could meet tomorrow, somewhere?' he drawled, but she managed to hedge the suggestion.

When she looked back through the archway Joshua had gone—and the brunette had gone as well. Good. Trouble was, Joshua would almost certainly be back.

'I suppose you think you're very clever,' Joshua stormed, breaking the icy silence that had driven home with them. It was nearly three, the roads had been icy and dangerous, and he had used all his concentration in getting them back in one piece. But now the danger was over and he could let rip.

'And just what is that supposed to mean?' Kelly stood her ground with a surprising amount of nerve. Or perhaps three gins and tonic had helped.

'It means that I won't have you behaving in that way while you're here with me.' He was out of his coat and throwing it on to a chair. Really, that was no way to treat camelhair!

'I was only *talking* to the man. D'you think I was trying to seduce him in the middle of a *party*?' she nearly shouted.

His face was like ice. 'Frankly, yes.'

'Great.' She tossed her head. 'I see.' Her gloves came

off and she threw them on the hall table. 'So it's all right for you to flirt with every woman in the room, but you expect a different set of rules from me. Is that it?' He was marching through to the drawing room, but she was right behind him, he wasn't getting out of it so easily. 'Is it? I said.' Her jacket was undone, she flung it on the settee.

His eyes were all over her. 'I choose my relationships with a little more discretion. If you think I'm going to let you come over here . . .'

'But you're not letting me come over, are you? You *ordered* me to Washington. What's the matter, Joshua? Are you beginning to regret your decision?' And for all the world she sounded just like her sister as she said it. There had been a play Jayne had been in once, the only one Kelly could remember, and she had stood straight and proud firing abuse at some man, and it was just like this—only this was for real . . .

'While you're a guest in my house you'll behave . . .'

'I'm not a guest, I'm a prisoner.' Her intricate coil of hair began coming undone and she tugged the rest of the grips out; that was better, now she could think straight.

'Jayne Osborn . . .'

Her eyes flashed. 'Don't you Jayne Osborn me!'

'I'll do as I . . .' Then he broke off, and turned away from her; his hands were at his throat and he began pulling off his bow-tie. His movements were aggressive and jerky, he looked as if he wished he had been strangling her. He went over to the trolley and poured himself a very stiff drink.

'Don't I get one?' Kelly asked quickly, not that she wanted it, but just to be awkward.

'You've had enough.'

'Really?' Her eyes widened, and her loose hair tumbled down round her bare shoulders. 'And how would you know about that? You were too busy chatting up all your women to notice anything I did!'

His tie was off now and he was undoing the top few buttons of his dress shirt. His deep suntan extended down his neck and throat and mingled with the dark hairs on his chest. Her eyes were riveted to them for several breathtaking seconds. Lord, the man was lethally attractive!

'Is that what bothers you?' he asked with experienced astuteness. He was taking off his jacket, picking up his glass of whisky, and there was an aura about him, a devastating, incredible aura of strength and excitement and undoubted virility ... He had spent the evening talking with women, most of them beautiful, glamorous, experienced, and, she guessed, more than willing to meet him on more intimate terms ... She could tell that his mind was still programmed to be receptive, and now all the women had gone and there was just Kelly—who he thought was Jayne ...

'Is that what's troubling you?' he repeated, and this time there was a low seductive edge to the richness of his voice. He took another sip of whisky, his eyes never leaving her own over the top of the glass. 'Is it pique? Do you wish I'd been a little more attentive?'

Kelly's voice froze. He looked exciting and dangerous and there was that smouldering fire in his eyes. 'No!' she said sharply, finding the use of her vocal cords again. 'That isn't what I meant.'

'Isn't it?' He was smiling secretly, but as if it was a secret they both shared. 'I don't believe you, my dear Jayne.' He put down his glass and her whole body trembled. 'I think you're angry—and perhaps you're right.' He slowly crossed the thick pile carpet, his feet were soundless, the only thing that Kelly could hear was the blood hammering in her ears. 'Maybe we shouldn't fight it. Maybe we should take advantage of our time together.' He was right in front of her now; she could see his chest rising and falling irregularly. But not half as bad as the panic leaping about in her own. His eyes held hers hypnotically. She couldn't move, couldn't fall, couldn't even begin to protest ... 'I'd forgotten,' he continued in that silky voice, 'you're an experienced woman.' He picked up a strand of her hair and caressed it with his fingers. 'You're used to men satisfying your needs——' there was an explosive silence, 'as I'm used to women satisfying mine ...' He tangled his long fingers into the thickness of her hair, and slowly, very slowly, he allowed his thumb to find the erratic pulse in her throat. His eyes were like dark fathoms of ecstasy, promising exquisite satisfaction and pleasure.

'Don't touch me,' she managed to whisper from a tight throat.

'Why not?' His breath was warm on her forehead. 'You've already proved that you won't break ...'

Her gasp was silenced by the gentle pressure of his mouth. He didn't kiss her exactly; at least, not in a way she had ever been kissed before. It was more as if he wanted to taste her—to eat her. He tugged sensuously at her full bottom lip, the hand behind her head drawing her inexorably nearer. There was no pleasure for him— no passion; he was like a scientist methodically carrying out an experiment.

If he had whispered her name, if he had seemed in the least bit moved by the experience, Kelly would have responded as her clamouring senses demanded ... But there was nothing endearing in his actions, just an experienced man once again beginning the act of seduction. His coldness gave Kelly the strength she needed.

'Leave me alone!' Her eyes and voice were like ice, although every nerve screamed at her in defiance. Never, ever, had anything like that happened to her. Her whole body ached with a strange longing.

He raised his head, the dark assessing eyes never leaving her face. And when he judged that she meant what she said, he untangled his hand from her hair with a philosophical shrug.

'Very well.' And he turned away from her and went back to his drink.

Kelly stared after him, her eyes riveted to his broad back. He could just turn around and walk away from her—like that!

He finished his whisky in one long draught, and when he faced her again, it looked as if a bitter taste had been left in his mouth.

'So the notorious lady turns out to be an ice-maiden.' Of all the things she had imagined he might say—she would never have thought of that!

'I see.' Still in a dream, she tottered round the back of a chair so that she would have something to cling on to. 'If I don't throw myself at your feet I'm frigid. Is that it?' She managed to laugh. 'My, my, you men certainly have a great opinion of yourselves. What's the matter, Joshua? Hasn't it happened before? Well, you know what they say, you can't win 'em all.'

His brief smile hardened the autocratic lines of his face. 'My dear Jayne, you misjudge me. I'm not interested in *winning* you—or winning anyone else, if it comes to that. I don't play games—least of all with women like you.'

Kelly felt as if she had been slapped across the face. 'And just exactly what is that supposed to mean?'

'Do I really have to be more explicit?' he drawled, strolling over towards her. Kelly gripped the back of the chair, her legs didn't seem to have the strength to run away. 'Haven't you been playing games for years?' His fingers delicately lifted a strand of her dark hair. 'The way you move your head . . .' he traced a line down her throat, '. . . the way you dress . . .' The back of his hand followed the contours of her breast and it was all she could do not to cry out in protest. 'Your awareness of your figure—the calculating movements of your body. All designed to please, Jayne—and they do, believe me.' Then the low, pulsating thread of his voice changed abruptly. Anger shone from his eyes and his hand coiled around her arm threateningly. 'But that's all it is—just promises. How many marriages have you wrecked? How many more children now come from broken homes? . . . And for what?' He laughed harshly. 'How many times have you given the tiniest part of yourself?'

'According to you I've gone straight from one man's bed to another.' The dream had vanished and Kelly was beside herself with fury. Did he really think that was how Jayne behaved? Could he despise her that much?

Or did he despise all women—everywhere? 'Let go of my arm!' she snarled, but he only laughed and shook her.

'You haven't the least idea of what I'm trying to say.'

'That's it—insult my intelligence now!'

'I'm not talking about you going to bed with a man—I'm not talking about the swift gratification of personal pleasure.' His face seared with evil delight as shock registered in her eyes. 'I'm talking about loving and sharing—and tenderness. Tell me, Jayne.' His voice dropped to any icy whisper. 'When did you ever give a man that?'

'Never!' she almost shouted.

'Good!' he replied equally quickly. His sensuous lips had parted and his even white teeth gleamed.

'What's that supposed to mean?' He had let go at last and Kelly was rubbing the painful white marks on her arm.

He shrugged, and all the fierce excitement went out of his face. The barrier had come down between them again; he was stone and ice all mixed up together.

'It means I was right. That, despite your notoriety, you have nothing whatever that interests me.'

She turned away and headed for the door. She wasn't really going to stand here one minute longer, whatever he might think. But he was quickly at her side, pulling her towards him. She struggled, but there was no urge to kiss her in his eyes.

'A man wants warmth from a woman. Passion, yes—but gentleness too.'

'I'm sure you get that from Glenda—*and* half the women in Washington,' she added nastily, twisting away from him.

'I am *not* having an affair with your stepmother!'

'I'm not *shocked*,' she assured him grandly. 'Daddy's been dead nearly three years—Glenda's an attractive woman, she was a lot younger than he—we all know she was a friend of yours before you introduced her to Daddy.'

Joshua grabbed her wrists, the dark eyes shrewdly

assessing. Then he gave an icy smile and let her go.
'You must understand, Jayne, that I never rekindle an
old affair on principle.' Her eyes widened at the coldness
in his voice. 'That surprises you? I don't see why. If a
relationship doesn't work out the first time, it's very
unlikely to succeed later.'

'Don't tell me you believe in love at first sight.' Why
had she said that? She turned and began gathering up
her jacket and bag.

'It all depends what you mean by love.' The quiet
firmness of his voice clutched at something inside her.
She couldn't answer him, and he didn't seem to expect
it.

'This is a fine old mess you've got yourself into,' Kelly
told herself fiercely. She undressed quickly, took off her
face, and peered at her weary reflection in growing
anger. Of course Joshua Brett didn't believe in love at
first sight—but did Kelly? Yesterday, at the airport,
hadn't something incredible happened to her? Was it
only yesterday—or was it years ago?

Oh no! She climbed into bed and switched off the
light ... but she was still awake at dawn—and dawn
came late in December. Joshua Brett was the most in-
human, impossible, chauvinistic male it had been her
misfortune to meet. He was ruthless, dangerous—a man
of ice ... She bit her bottom lip, remembering. But he
was also the most devastating man she had ever kissed.
She should be recalling those moments after the party
with humiliation—and tomorrow she would. But right
now, alone in her bed, all she could think of was the feel
of his hands on her body, his lips exploring her own ...
And here it came again, the sharp excitement deep inside
her that demanded a far more intimate fulfilment. The
gratification of personal pleasure, Joshua had called it,
and Kelly felt sick. Okay, it wasn't love. Only the
Osborn women didn't seem able to indulge in affairs
without becoming emotionally involved. Jayne was a
case in point and instinct told Kelly it would be the
same with herself.

And it would be a mistake to fall in love with Joshua

Brett, wouldn't it? Instinct told her that, as well. But unfortunately, she had a feeling that it was too late.

CHAPTER FIVE

IT was almost ten o'clock when Kelly staggered into the kitchen the following morning. She blinked as she pulled up the window blind; the sun was dazzling, bouncing back at her from about four inches of snow. She changed the date on the calendar—December 23rd. Two days to Christmas. Hurray for the festive spirit!

There was no sign of Joshua, no sign of anyone having made an early breakfast, either. Did that mean that the man slept late after a party? That he was human, after all? She groped in the fridge and found the orange juice. Lovely. She sank down on a chair and leaned her elbows on the table. No, he wasn't human, he was cold and ruthless and he didn't love her—but then he didn't love anyone else either. And she didn't care. She really didn't care. He was thirty-two—far too old for her—far too sophisticated and experienced. Her hair fell over her face and she wound a strand of it behind her ear. She was in America—it was Christmas, surely there must be some way of enjoying the time . . .

The phone rang and she stared at it—it rang again and she picked it up. She didn't want·Joshua in here answering it.

'Hullo.'

'Jayne?' It was her stepmother.

Kelly tried to think quickly, but couldn't. 'Er . . .' she began.

'Glenda?' It was Joshua, he sounded sleepy; he must have had a telephone extension in his room.

Kelly put down the receiver and left them to it. Wow! That had been close. She wandered across and put some muffins in the toaster, then started to search the fridge again, this time for the maple syrup.

She was scraping butter on to the muffins when Joshua came into the room. He looked ruffled and unshaven, a short towelling robe seemed to have been hastily tied. Beneath it he had long bare legs and bare feet.

'She wants to speak to you,' he said, matter-of-factly. He didn't seem suspicious. Was Glenda?

Kelly willed him to leave, but he didn't, and there was nothing she could do but use the phone that was hanging on the kitchen wall.

'Hullo again, Glenda,' she began cautiously. Joshua had his back to her—he was helping himself to her muffins—cheek!

'Kelly? That is you, isn't it?' Glenda sounded anything but happy.

'Yes. And a Merry Christmas to you too.'

'Is Joshua still there?'

'That's right.' Kelly could have laughed if it hadn't been so serious. 'It looks as if we're in for a white Christmas.'

'What game are the two of you playing?' came the crisp voice from Florida. Then, realising Kelly couldn't answer that, Glenda tried another way. 'Was it Jayne's idea? Has she gone off somewhere?' and for five minutes the two women played a crazy charade.

Joshua ate both the muffins, and then began making the coffee. Kelly glared at his back . . . he really was a superb shape . . .

'Kelly!'

'I—I'm still here, Glenda.'

'Good. Then listen to me.' Kelly was all ears. 'He doesn't suspect—I know that from what he's just been saying to me.' Her stepdaughter could well imagine, but with the wretched man still standing in the kitchen she could hardly ask. 'So if you do anything—*anything*, Kelly, d'you hear me?—to mess up my plans . . .'

'How's it going?' Kelly asked, trying to find out a bit more about her stepmother's loan.

Glenda sighed. 'If I knew that I wouldn't be on the phone now. He won't tell me what's happening—he says he's still looking into my partner. Have I told you about Al?'

'No.' Joshua was messing about at the sink. He was staying here on purpose, she was sure of it. The white towelling robe certainly set off his terrific suntan. How had he acquired it? Water-skiing? Sailing in Chesapeake Bay? Or did he normally take an autumnal break in the West Indies? She could picture him on some exotic beach with a beautiful girl ... There were little dark hairs curling against the bronzed tautness of his thigh. It was a remarkably scanty robe to be wearing in winter. If it had been any shorter ... Kelly swallowed. 'Sorry, Glenda, what did you say?'

Eventually her stepmother rang off. No, she hadn't wanted to speak to Joshua again. One thing seemed to be certain—it looked as if he had been speaking the truth. They weren't having an affair—if they had been Glenda would never have dismissed him like that.

'I suppose you think that's very funny,' said Kelly, when she had finally said her goodbyes. 'Those were my muffins and you've—you've eaten them, both of them!' Didn't they say the best kind of defence was attack? She looked up at him through her dark curtain of tumbled hair. He didn't look suspicious. Maybe Glenda was right.

'They're no good if they're left to get cold,' he said mildly. 'There's plenty more in the bread bin.'

'Thanks.'

'You're welcome,' he replied, as if he had been a check-out operator in a supermarket store.

But Kelly wasn't fooled by his supposed good humour. Be careful, Glenda had said, and that was just what she had to be. She sliced a couple more muffins in half and rammed them into the toaster. She must have been out of her mind to agree to come. Where was Jayne now? Swanning around in the Indian Ocean? It was all right for some!

She clattered and banged about for a bit, and Joshua just sat at the table and watched her. Every time she passed anywhere near she had to step over his out-stretched legs. 'Great legs,' she muttered to herself, 'big feet! . . .' 'And you know what they say about men with big feet,' she suddenly heard her sister say. Kelly went hot all over—her sister really had a wicked sense of fun ... And was it true? If a man had big feet was he built big everywhere else as well? Lord—she was being *obscene* ...

'You all right? You look a bit rough,' said Joshua suddenly.

She glared at him—but not as far down as his feet. 'You don't look so bright yourself.'

And he didn't. He looked different today. Weary, less aggressive, almost as if he had lain awake all night, thinking ...

Now his eyes were half-closed slits—watching her. Last night's evident distaste seemed to have changed into a reluctant admiration for her.

Her heart fluttered and she wanted to hold out her hand to him ... No, that would be fatal. But somehow their relationship was changing ... and then she realised that he was beginning to look at her in exactly the same way as he had looked at all those women last night.

She had to get away from him—it was absolutely essential.

'Glenda invited me to Florida for Christmas!' she almost squeaked.

'Is that a fact?'

No, it wasn't, but he didn't know that. Surely Glenda wouldn't mind if she just turned up—if Joshua was supposed to agree ...

'But I trust you told her that we're going to the Blue Ridge instead,' and then he remembered that he hadn't heard her mention any such thing, and a dark frown severed the space between his eyes.

'You're not really serious?' said Kelly, mumbling through a mouthful of buttery muffin. 'Have you seen the snow out there?' She waved a hand towards the window, then wiped her chin. 'Where are we going to stay? Where are the Blue Ridge Mountains, anyway?' She poured some maple syrup on to the other half and watched it ooze down among the holes.

'You enjoying that?' asked Joshua, a little disdainfully.

What was the matter with him? Didn't he like seeing people enjoy their food?

He watched her tuck into the feast for a few more minutes, then he gradually seemed to remember what she had said.

'D'you really mean to tell me you've never heard of the Blue Ridge Mountains?' he asked imperiously.

'Did I *say* I hadn't heard of them?' Kelly contemplated having another muffin—then decided against it. *'Ooh, take me back to the Blue Ridge . . .'* she started singing in a silly voice.

'All right—all right,' he held his head in agony. 'Now I know why you've never been in a musical.'

'Got a hang-over, have you?'

'You're very perky this morning,' was all she got for a reply.

'Trouble you, does it?'

Something mysterious flickered in his eyes—it made her feel uneasy.

'Is the new perky you going to be more amenable?' There was no emotion in his voice.

'Amenable to what?' she asked suspiciously.

He leant both elbows on the table and the front of his robe gaped open. Kelly tried not to notice, but it wasn't easy. Everything about Joshua Brett, every tousled hair, every inch of that taut, smooth skin, seemed very desirable, very touchable . . .

'Maybe we can have a Merry Christmas, after all,' he said softly, almost as if he could read her mind. 'Glenda didn't really invite you to Florida, did she?'

Kelly gulped and tried to think straight. 'I can go to Florida if I want.'

'But she didn't invite you.'

'Not—not exactly.' There was nothing else she could say—all he had to do was pick up the phone.

'And you don't really want to spend Christmas with your stepmother and all her boy-friends . . .' He reached across and took hold of her hand, his thumb gently caressing the inside of her wrist. 'Wouldn't you much rather come with me to the Blue Ridge in a nice—cosy—cabin?' He strung out the words deliberately—it was perfect torture.

She snatched her hand away and clutched together the fronts of the flimsy concoction that Jayne had called a dressing gown. It was practically transparent, and Joshua was looking at her with those big brown eyes . . .

'Changed your tune, haven't you?' she managed to croak.

'How d'you mean?' he taunted. Oh, how he enjoyed seeing her squirm!

'I seem to remember you saying—not so very long ago—that you weren't interested in me.'

Anger momentarily tightened his mouth, but this time he chose to brush it away. 'I've been thinking,' he shrugged, 'it's only natural—your reluctance—if you thought I was having an affair with Glenda.'

'Thanks!' But she was still suspicious.

He sat back in the chair and folded strong arms across his powerful chest. 'But now you know I'm not—so you don't have to be inhibited.'

'Look here,' Kelly leapt up from her side of the table and clattered the plates in the sink, 'I'm not interested in . . . in becoming number nine hundred and ninety-nine in your harem. Even if it isn't Glenda, you're not exactly celibate, are you?'

'Hardly.'

'So there!' But that sounded childish, and she was cross with herself—and confused. 'If I'm just supposed to have got out of one mess I'm hardly likely to want to land myself with a whole lot more.'

'*Supposed* to have got out of a mess?' He was quick to leap at her mistake. 'You mean you haven't?'

'No—no—okay, so I *have* just got out of a mess.' Kelly grabbed the washing up liquid and squirted far too much into the bowl. 'But I have a rule, you see, like you do,' she added with sudden inspiration, and now it was Joshua's turn to demand that she make herself more clear.

'*You* don't rekindle an old affair on principle—and I don't *begin* an affair until the man loves me!' There, let him get out of that. She waved the dish-mop triumphantly.

'Believe in getting your pound of flesh, don't you?' he said nastily. Then he got up as well and thrust his hands into the large patch pockets.

Kelly returned to the washing up, but he was still there, standing somewhere behind her; all the skin down her back prickled. She was mad to be having this argument with him. She ought to keep out of his way. He was a big man, dangerous, and he looked especially rough and earthy this morning, with his tousled hair and dark smudgy chin. He smelt warm and musky—a sort of bitter-sweet maleness. Lord, there she went again, first his feet—now his body ... What was the matter with her? Why this sudden interest in his intimate anatomy?

She couldn't make the washing up last any longer, and she finally had to turn round and reach for a towel. He was there, leaning against the edge of the table, his face was a mask—but his dark, shrewd eyes seemed to swallow her.

'Why do I get the feeling that you very seldom tell me the truth?' he began carefully.

Kelly felt herself go red and quickly turned away.

'Answer me,' he growled. 'Are you playing some private game?'

'Oh, yes, I'm full of games.' She composed herself with difficulty. 'This is just the sort of Christmas I planned; nice warm climate, among friends ... You're the one who's playing games,' she added savagely, and she was really cross, because it was all his fault that she had been dragged here ... 'What gave you the right to play the heavy father anyway? You don't know me. You don't know what it's like trying to live in London and make a success of it in the theatre. It's all very well for you to get all high and mighty because I've had a few unfortunate love-affairs ... But if you'd been a *friend*, really cared about me, you'd have invited me here to have a holiday—to recover.'

He laughed harshly. 'That's rich!'

'Yes, recover!' She could see Jayne's anguish right now. 'Understand? So don't sit there pretending you want me to . . . to . . .'

'Yes, Jayne, what exactly do I want you to do?'

'Oh—go to hell!' She made a dive for the door, but he was there first.

'Is this much true?' He took both her shoulders in his powerful grip. 'Jayne, look at me, have you been ill? Were you really in love this time?'

Her eyes flitted to his face, but quickly darted away again. 'I just need to be left alone,' she whispered. Why on earth did she have to feel so ashamed?

His face hardened. 'Perhaps that's as well—we don't really suit each other.' Then he let her go and opened the kitchen door. 'I had intended leaving early,' he said, following her out into the hall. 'But shall we say twelve—we'll have a nice leisurely drive. And don't forget to pack your Wellington boots,' he called after her as she ran away.

Wellington boots! Who did he think her sister was? And no, they certainly didn't suit each other, *anyway*!

Kelly had to dig deeply into Jayne's wardrobe to find something suitable to wear. The cord jeans were her own, even her sister hadn't objected to their soft moss green. Kelly would have liked to have packed a few of her own floppy jumpers, but Jayne had kept on about maintaining her image. So when she had washed her hair and showered, Kelly had to put on one of Jayne's short, skinny-rib sweaters, the colour was a perfect match—but were cabins in the Blue Ridge centrally heated?

She was halfway through packing her nylon roll-bag when the enormity of what she was doing suddenly struck her. Here she was, calmly doing as he said while she waited for her hair to dry . . . Going off into the wilds with a man whom—well, she was certainly *aware* of in a peculiar way. And there he had sat at breakfast, practically asking her to have an affair . . .

Kelly plonked down on the edge of the bed and tried to clear her mind. But thoughts kept coming back, as they had done all through the hours of darkness. Joshua downstairs last night, stroking her hair, touching her body—*admitting* that she excited him ... Did he really find her physically attractive? *Her*. *Kelly*. She stood up and took stock of herself in the dressing table mirror. Her still-damp hair hung loosely, with no make-up on she looked exactly like Kelly. Last night she had looked like Jayne.

Yes, that was the difference. That was what excited him—Jayne, the complete Jayne—her looks, her experience—and everything else that she was supposed to be.

Kelly sighed. So if she stayed like this everything would be all right, wouldn't it? A man of Joshua's experience would hardly remain interested in someone who looked as ordinary as she, and perhaps in the mountains, if he was enjoying himself, she might be able to persuade him to lend Glenda the money. Once that was safe she could go home.

She went downstairs with her doubts shelved rather than resolved, and found Joshua packing the car. It was a large white station wagon—the black Lincoln was staying at home. Yes, he looked totally different today. Gone were the dark city clothes and crisp white shirts. Even the lethal black polo sweater and jeans had had a certain sophistication. Now he was wearing dark brown cords and matching shirt, and a thick cream sweater with a chunky rib. His shoes were suede, heavier than the type he normally wore ... they all made him look strong and immensely capable—tough.

It was very cold outside and he shouted to her to get back indoors and put on a coat. The girl from next door was hanging around again, he didn't seem to mind *her* company.

'That's it all in, then,' he said, eventually coming into the kitchen where she was making a last cup of coffee before they left. 'Is there anything you want to do first—any shopping on the way?'

'No! Where's Rosey? Does she want some coffee?'

'Rosey?' He obviously forgot his women the moment they were out of sight. 'No, she's gone off home.' Then his eyes were shrewd again.

'No phone calls you want to make?'

She set a mug of coffee carefully in front of him on the kitchen table.

'I spoke to Glenda this morning . . .' but as soon as she had said it, she knew exactly what was coming next.

'Wouldn't you like to speak to your sister? There won't be any phones where we're going.'

Your sister . . . your sister! Even now he hadn't called her Kelly. Perhaps he had forgotten her name. Charming!

'I—er—I'm not sure where she's going to be . . .'

'That's splendid—*splendid*.' He was really angry—so angry that the edges of his lips had turned white. 'Haven't you got some idea—couldn't you *try*? It is Christmas. Damn it all, Jayne, you're the only real family she's got!' They stared at each other; there was absolutely nothing Kelly could say. And then, to her horror, he picked up the wall telephone and punched out a dozen odd numbers straight off. Was he actually phoning the flat in Hampstead? Surely he didn't know the number by heart? His connection rang and rang as he held the receiver in mid-air, then after five long, long minutes he slammed it down again.

'There you are,' she muttered hopelessly, 'she's obviously away . . .'

'You little . . .' He grabbed her by the shoulders and then suddenly pushed her away, as if he couldn't trust himself. She went tottering back across the kitchen and nearly landed up in the sink. 'I certainly did the right thing bringing you over here, you—you unfeeling little bitch! Your own kid sister, only eighteen years old . . .'

'Nineteen—she's nearly twenty,' Kelly blurted out.

'Oh, great, that really makes a difference, does it?'

Kelly rubbed the elbow that she had banged on the stainless steel draining board. 'She isn't a kid—will you stop calling her that? And she wouldn't thank you for all this fuss and bother about where she spends

Christmas.' Kelly had left her hair hanging loose today, and it was flying about now all over the place. She wound it behind her ear with a muffled oath and missed a strange look in Joshua's eye. 'She's old enough to earn her own living and stay with whoever she likes at Christmas,' she added for good measure.

'Who exactly? Which friend?'

Kelly shrugged. 'How should I know? Maybe you wish you'd invited her over instead of me.' For some odd reason she found herself holding her breath for his answer.

It didn't come. He gave an ugly smile. 'I'm going to make this a Christmas you're never likely to forget!' The urbane sophistication had finally gone. Before her now was a hard granite of a man, a ruthless man who would leave the rules of civilisation behind him on the streets of Washington. Just in time she had had a glimpse of what it might truly be like with him—miles away from anyone.

'I'm getting out of here,' she began, but he grabbed her arm.

'You're coming with me—understand?'

A Christmas to remember! Kelly didn't know whether to cry or have hysterics.

They left late, which put him in an even worse mood—if that were possible. They had another row; should they have lunch before—or on the way? In the end Joshua had practically dragged her out of the house, and they stopped three miles up the road at McDonald's to have a hamburger.

Bit of a comedown, wasn't it, for the great Joshua Brett to be eating here amongst the pot plants and trellis and shining plastic tables. She watched him line up at the counter, just like everyone else, and afterwards, as he carried the tray over to their table ... He had a special way of moving, slowly now, but with a lethal, male grace. It was all there, from the shrewd eyes, the dynamic self-assurance, right down to those tantalisingly narrow hips ... She swallowed and unwrapped her burger. He didn't really look like Joshua Brett of Space

Design U.K. He looked more . . . more . . .

'Are you going to keep looking at that beefburger, or do you intend eating it?' he asked nastily.

Kelly glared, then bit. He was just more exasperating—even more dangerous . . . It began snowing again and the people just leaving had to run to their car. Joshua looked at his watch and sighed, but Kelly chewed more slowly, she had no intention of getting indigestion.

It was two-thirty when they left the Capital Beltway and headed south-west on Interstate 66. There were plenty of cars on the road, most of them packed with holidaymakers. Some of them had Christmas trees strapped to the roof-rack. Joshua roared down the outside lane, his citizens' band radio tuned to get news of any approaching speed-check. Joshua Brett speeding? Joshua Brett breaking the law! But then this wasn't Washington, was it? Out in the wilds, what else could she expect?

They drove most of the way in silence. He knew exactly where he was going, which was a relief because she didn't like the idea of having to navigate. After a while they turned west on to a much quieter road that rolled around farmland. There was more snow about now, not on the road itself, which had been mechanically cleared, but the fields looked as if they had been covered for several days. There were only one or two brown patches revealed by the sun's midday warmth.

'I hope the road's open,' said Joshua, more or less to himself.

Kelly glanced at him in horror. 'What if it isn't—do we go back?'

'No such luck—we just go round the long way.' Silence again. They saw one or two cars going in the opposite direction—towards civilisation—but there was no one else heading towards the mountains . . . at last Kelly saw them.

They *were* blue! A sort of hazy, mauvey blue; then the road closed in leaving the farmland behind, and they were climbing through a forest of pines. She felt excited in a curious sort of way. The journey hadn't taken as long as she had expected, not two hours yet, although she had no idea how much farther they had to go.

Joshua began following the signs to the Skyline Drive. And then there was a hut, and a real live Ranger, and a notice about the state of the road and that snow-tyres were advisable.

'We had to close everything up at the weekend,' the Ranger said, leaning out of his window and smiling down at them. 'The roads are okay now—but it's freezing hard.' He was about to ask for the admission money when Joshua waved his season ticket at him. 'Going far, are you?' he asked instead. 'I'm afraid you won't find any of the visitor centres open.'

'How about the restaurants?' Joshua's English accent seemed out of place, somehow.

'No, sir—'fraid not.' Then he seemed to realise who he was speaking to. 'It's Mr Brett, isn't it?' He smiled at Kelly, as if that made her welcome, as well. 'Come up for the Bird Count, have you?'

The two men talked for a bit, and Kelly found that she was feeling more than a little relieved. It wasn't that she had disbelieved him, exactly, yet counting birds at Christmas was a bit far-fetched. But it seemed to be official—well, that was something.

At last Joshua drove away and the goodbye smile slowly faded from his face. 'The sun's getting low—but I think we'll just stop and let you see the valley . . .' And after a couple of winding miles during which she had glimpses of an incredible view on the right, he pulled into a layby that called itself *Shenandoah Valley Overlook*.

They both climbed out of the station-wagon and the icy wind cut into them like a knife. It really was freezing up here; the snow was piled against the low wall in hard, icy lumps. Joshua held her arm unconsciously, Kelly knew he didn't really mean it.

He didn't say anything for a while, and she just stared. Shenandoah. The name conjured scenes of battles, the Civil War, men in blue or grey fighting each other;

families on opposing sides . . . It wasn't a tight, narrow valley as she had imagined, but more of a rolling plain with scattered farms, and houses, frozen lakes—and of course the river . . . but there were some mountains beyond it—and a whole lot more beyond that.

'That's Signal Knob,' said Joshua, pointing to a ridge on the nearest range. 'On Massanutten mountain. It was a communication post during the Civil War—you can see why they chose it.'

Kelly could. Here, on the northern tip of the Skyline Drive, you could see everything around for miles.

'See where those farms are?' She nodded absently. 'Indians used to keep deer and bison down there.' He left her in peace again—and she was glad of it.

'I suppose it sounds silly,' she admitted, their hostility forgotten for the moment while they were faced with so much history, 'but I sort of imagined the Civil War, and the Indian troubles, as happening miles and miles away. Not here—a couple of hours from Washington.' She shrugged, knowing she wasn't explaining herself very well. 'It sort of makes it all seem very real.'

'I know what you mean. Bit different from reading all about it at school in England.' She nodded, amazed that he seemed to feel the same, and they stood there, staring out at the valley. 'You can imagine how I felt,' Joshua said quietly, 'when I first came out. One minute I'm wrapped up in the Space race—but when you come out here and realise what it was like only a hundred years ago . . .'

'What are those other mountains—beyond?' she asked, sensing that, for some reason, he needed prompting.

'They're the Allegheny Mountains—and did you know that part of the Blue Ridge is on the Appalachian Trail?'

She didn't know—but she had heard about the Appalachian Trail. It was the sort of place people walked once, then lectured about it for the rest of their lives. It was a wild place—hadn't she heard about bears?

'Come on,' he said, as they screwed their eyes up against the setting sun, 'we'd better be going. I don't want to try and find the cabin in the dark.'

'Is it—er—remote, this cabin?' asked Kelly, when they had climbed back into the car and she had stopped shivering.

Joshua pulled on to the road carefully, the slushy midday puddles were already iron-hard.

'I suppose you'd call it remote,' he admitted after a while. 'What's the matter, Jayne? Beginning to get worried, are you?'

'No,' she lied. 'Ought I to be?'

The humour left his eyes as he glanced at her. 'If I were in your position,' he said grimly, 'I would be.'

CHAPTER SIX

'I'LL clear the steps and you can start unloading,' said Joshua, rummaging in the back of the station-wagon for the snow shovel. They had left the metalled road half an hour ago, the track through the woods had been snowy but passable. Joshua had driven in the tyre marks made by the Rangers' trucks. At least some other form of life passed this way—it was Kelly's only consolation.

So where were they now—where were the steps he was supposed to be clearing? The light had almost gone and Kelly peered round cautiously. The winter forest peered back at her with frosty eyes.

'Come on—I said unload.' Joshua had the back hatch open now and the cold air gripped Kelly's ears.

'But there isn't anything here,' she protested, climbing down and marching round to the back of the vehicle.

'Expected the Holiday Inn, did you?' They had pulled off the track in an area that was too small to be called a layby. Above them the trees were clinging to an almost perpendicular slope; below the track wound its crazy way downwards. This level bit of ground seemed little more than a shelf.

Joshua was putting on a pair of insulated Wellington boots. Surely they couldn't really be staying here ... and then she saw it, up amongst the trees. The gardener's shed in their old Surrey home had been bigger.

'If you think I'm staying up there, you've got another think coming!' she declared angrily.

'And if you think I'm taking you anywhere else, *you've* got another think coming. Let's get this car unloaded. The sooner we do that the sooner we can have a hot drink and warm up.'

Kelly groaned inwardly and started heaving boxes. At least it was one way of keeping warm. After a few moments she could see the steps; Joshua had already

cleared about half a dozen, so she started piling everything on the bottom step, which looked as if it had been
made out of a railway sleeper.

'Believe in travelling light, don't you?' she muttered,
when he came back down to see if she had finished.

'You have to take plenty of food at this time of the
year—never know if you're likely to get snowed up.'

Kelly tottered to the steps with another box. He was
joking, wasn't he? Surely they wouldn't have come if
there had been the slightest chance of that?

The steps were clear—all seventeen of them. Kelly
took one of the smaller boxes up first; Joshua was right
behind her. There was a light on in the porch now; as
she drew closer she had her first really good look at the
cabin, which was eyeball-to-eyeball with the birds in the
trees. It was built out of the side of the hill on stilts. It
had a steep, snow-laden roof that curved down to cover
the porch. For some reason it reminded Kelly of a gin-
gerbread house from fairy story days. But then there
was no time for further discoveries, because it was back
down again for another box, and another . . . By the
time they had finished it was really dark and the first
stars were beginning to shine.

'The kitchen's over there,' said Joshua, waving into
the gloom. 'I'll get some more lamps lit and see to the
fire . . .' and he left Kelly standing in the middle of a
pile of boxes and bedding gear.

'Am I expected to see to all this by myself?' she asked
angrily.

He glanced over his shoulder. 'The kitchen's your department—I've no intention of interfering.'

'You've done nothing else for the past few days—
don't let me stop you now.'

'You won't stop me doing anything I might want to,
my dear Jayne.'

Jayne. Jayne. Always Jayne. It was totally irrational,
but she really was getting fed up with it.

She flopped down into a chair. 'I'm tired and I'm
hungry—and I've had enough.' It was a comfortable
chair, large and leathery. In fact, the whole room wasn't

bad really, if you happened to like the bare rustic look. There was a huge stone chimney-breast that disappeared up through the ceiling. All the walls were logs held together with some sort of plaster instead of mud. There were bookcases, tables, all in old stripped pine, and several rugs in a woven Aztec-type design. Sporting prints and hunting trophies hung on the chunky walls. In all, it looked as if it had been furnished to some sort of plan. In summer you could have plants hanging from the beams, and vases of wild flowers . . . But that was a ridiculous thing to think. She would never be here in summer.

The first logs were beginning to crackle now and Joshua stood up, brushing off his hands. The way he did it made her remember that first evening in Washington, when he had put more logs on the drawing room fire. She had felt trapped then—and she felt trapped now. Something was closing in on her. It had begun in Mclean, but here, in this isolated cabin, she felt it even more. It was as if all life's devilish temptations were about to be dangled in front of her. And was Joshua the devil's messenger?

For a few short weeks she was being cast out into the world as it really was. All her life she had been protected, up till now. First at home and, more recently, at university. Where, although she hated to admit it, she had been able to push work between herself and any intimate relationship that might have developed. Romantic attachments hadn't interested her. Hadn't she believed herself incapable of falling in love? Incapable—or frightened? Kelly didn't like to think about the answer.

Almost unseeing, she stared at Joshua as he prowled around the room. Was she really so very different from Jayne? Hadn't they both tried to opt out of responsibilities? Kelly had chosen to work hard—and Jayne had chosen men.

For a brief moment she had a vision of what it might be like to live under Joshua's protection. There would be irresistible excitement, wild days and wild nights . . .

But for how long? How could she cope with life when his interest had waned?

It was silly, of course, Joshua wasn't really the devil's messenger—or was he? Hadn't he opened a secret door in her soul—a door that she had never dared look behind before? Kelly had the distinct feeling that soon she would have to meet herself face to face.

It took a great deal of courage not to leap up and run screaming for the door. Instead she stood up and shivered, wandering over to the fire and rubbing her arms.

'If you're cold I suggest you get busy,' said Joshua, lighting table lamps and sorting out the bags of clothing. She was suddenly surprised that he had let her sit for so long.

'I can't cook,' she admitted, and he just stared at her. 'I *can't*,' she repeated, shaking her head. The ironic thing was, Jayne had a Cordon Bleu diploma, but she was pretty certain he had no idea of that.

'Typical!' He ran irate fingers through the dark tangle of his hair. 'Then you'll have to learn, won't you?'

She shrugged. 'It's your stomach.'

He groaned. 'Come on—you can still unload the boxes,' and he led her through to what he obviously called the kitchen but which was really no bigger than a cupboard. 'Tins there, vegetables down there—and that's the freezer.'

'You mean there's electricity in this place?'

'Either that or the glow-worms put in overtime,' he snapped.

'Good of them.'

His eyes darkened. 'Yes.'

He left her to it, and she clattered everything away. It was a very well equipped kitchen—for a cupboard. It reminded her of a tiny yacht's galley.

Joshua went outside, back down to the car, she guessed, so she took the empty boxes back to the living room for him to deal with later, and had a bit of a poke about while he was out of the way.

The front porch, which they had climbed up to, was supported on stilts, as was the front half of the cabin.

But the back portion nestled right into the mountain. There was a tiny back porch, from which you could step off straight into the woods. It looked as if one end of the back porch had been enclosed to make the kitchen, yet the extension looked bigger than that tiny kitchen. Kelly investigated further and discovered that another sliding door led to a tiny shower room and a loo. Well, that was something. She came back out. So that only left one more problem; where was she supposed to sleep?

She heard Joshua's footsteps outside, so she stepped back into the kitchen section and put on the kettle. The cooker was electric, and he hadn't turned on a generator. That meant they must be connected in the normal way. So were there other cabins nearby? Where did the Rangers live?

The kettle boiled and she made the tea, searching round afterwards for something to eat.

'There's a fruit cake in one of the tins,' said Joshua's voice from the doorway, and Kelly jumped. How long had he been there? She glanced at him uncertainly through her thick curtain of hair. He was leaning against the door jamb, his dark eyes watching her shrewdly. She felt jittery inside and her fingers started trembling.

She found the cake and began undoing the clinging wrapper. Then she rummaged for a knife and wound the soft, floppy hair behind her ear.

'Don't do that!' said Joshua sharply, and it was so unexpected that she nearly dropped the knife.

'Don't do what?' she managed to say, although her heart was pounding. Why did he have to torment her like this, just standing there looking so tall and lethal?

'Leave your hair alone.' He took one short step to reach her side, unwinding the hair and letting it fall loosely against her cheek. 'That's better—it suits you. What's the matter?' His lips twitched. 'Why so jumpy?'

'I'm not—I just don't like being watched, that's all.' She tried to shrug him away, but he wouldn't go. His hand was still in her hair, his thumb gently tracing the outline of her cheekbone. A dull throbbing sensation began beating in time with her heart. But it had nothing to do with her heart; it was deep, deep down inside her. Kelly held her breath and fought frantically with the demon trying to get out . . .

'I rather thought actresses liked being looked at.' Joshua's warm breath drifted across her face, but she knew he was laughing at her.

'Not this actress.' She picked up the knife and began attacking the cake. 'Not today.'

He let his hand fall. 'Of course, I forgot, it's all an act, isn't it? Even this——' his eyes raked over her, 'this new innocent image. It suits you, Jayne. No make-up, no sophisticated hair-do. It's a pleasant change from . . .'

'All your glamorous women in Washington?' It was out before she could stop herself.

'If I didn't know better, I'd say those were the words of a jealous woman.'

'Well, you do know better—and I'm not. Now, would you mind getting out of the way. I'm trying to find some plates.'

'Sure.' He moved aside obligingly. 'But there is only the two of us—why have you cut up all the cake?'

Damn! Now it would go dry. 'Just get out—go on!' and he did so, but there was a taunting smile on his lips as he left.

'Whose place is this?' asked Kelly, when she eventually carried the tray through to the living room. The logs were ablaze now, the room was even beginning to feel warm. Only now did she take off her jacket.

'Is that the only coat you've brought?' asked Joshua, moving all the bird books to one end of the coffee table so that she could put the tray down.

'I was summoned to *Washington*, not half way up a mountain. If I'd known that I would have brought a polar-suit.' He was right though, this extravagant little jacket of Jayne's ended just below her waist. If she fell over in the snow her bottom would freeze. Even her old duffel coat would have been better than that.

'I asked whose cabin this was,' she reminded him, grudgingly pouring out the tea. She had no intention of waiting on him permanently—the next meal would be his turn.

'It's mine.' The large pottery cups suited his strong hands.

'Do you come up here often?'

'Only in the . . .' She glared at him and he changed his mind. 'As often as I can,' he said instead.

'Why?' This might not be getting them anywhere, but it was a nice safe topic while she sorted out how to approach what was really on her mind; like—where was she going to sleep?

'If you have to ask why I come here, then you wouldn't understand the answer.'

'Try me.'

He shrugged. 'Sometimes I need to get away.'

'You mean when Washington gets too hot for *you*?' She felt like adding, '*touché*.'

One eyebrow lifted. 'Perhaps.'

'I would have thought this was a perfect place to bring a mistress—not to run away from them.' Kelly couldn't help herself, she had to make him hate her—that way she was safe.

'I never run away from anyone, Jayne.' Then the ice in his voice melted as he settled back in the chair and continued, 'I haven't brought anyone up here—simply because it hasn't worked out that way.'

'You mean none of your girl-friends actually wanted to tramp around a mountain counting birds at Christmas?'

'Something like that.' He took a piece of cake, but his eyes never left her face.

'You do surprise me.' Kelly bit into her own cake. Heavens, at this rate she would be putting on pounds! 'You don't actually like women, do you?' This time she even surprised herself.

'They're quite delightful—in their place.'

Kelly's eyes widened. 'And I suppose you think that's cooking your meals, cleaning your house, and . . .'

'That's right, Jayne—say it.'

She glared at him. 'And warming your bed.'

'And you, of all people, should see nothing wrong with that.'

'Of course not.' Kelly managed to keep her voice level. 'I told you, if two people love each other . . .'

'You don't know the meaning of the word,' he almost snarled.

'And neither do you—so that makes us quits.'

'But I don't go round wrecking people's lives in an attempt to find it.'

'Just as well,' she snapped, 'because you probably wouldn't recognise it if it leapt up and hit you in the face.'

She expected him to erupt with anger, but for some strange reason he was deeply thoughtful.

'You could be right.' He was looking into the fire, not at her. 'I don't have time for a permanent woman in my life . . . my company has to come first.'

Kelly felt cold inside. 'You don't have to explain to me.'

'I wasn't,' he said quickly. The dark eyes searched her face. 'You're the one who brought love into the conversation.'

She raised her chin. 'Only so you'd know where we stand.'

His eyelids drooped. 'And where exactly is that, my dear Jayne?'

'Nowhere.' She didn't wait for his reply, but made an excuse of getting more hot water for the teapot.

He caught her while she was filling the kettle. He came up behind her and two large hands encircled her waist.

'I don't think you mean that,' he whispered into her hair. Kelly put down the kettle with a clatter, and he laughed and turned her round—and there was nowhere else she could go. 'You don't mean it, do you?' he taunted. His eyes were dark and smouldering and the sensuous curve of his mouth came closer . . .

Kelly couldn't move and she didn't want to. His

thumbs had eased beneath her sweater and were tracing little lines of fire over her bare midriff. She was dissolving . . . melting against the long, hard length of him as he drew her even nearer. She gazed up at him imploringly, although whether imploring him to stop—or not to stop, she could not be sure.

He kissed her. It was a slow, delicious kiss that sent her arms up, up and coiling around his neck, her fingers tangling into the thick dark hair at his nape. Instinctively her body arched against him, and as she did so his kiss hardened and the hands on her body became aggressively possessive.

That should have been the time when she pushed him away, but instead something went wild inside her and she found herself responding with equal fire. Everything was heat and excitement and crazy sensation.

At last Joshua drew her away from him, his breath was ragged and bright eyes crackled in a taut, passionate face.

'I knew it,' he whispered.

But Kelly wasn't sure what he knew. Everything was still a blissful whirl—she didn't want him talking to her . . .

She moistened her lips with unknowing provocation, and he groaned and began kissing her again . . . A minute—an hour?—later and she was dimly aware of being carried through to the living room, but as he gently tumbled her on to the settee she finally came to her senses. What did he know? That he could, oh so easily, seduce her? Was he just experimenting again?

'What are you doing? Joshua—no,' she muttered stupidly, pushing him away and struggling to her feet. 'You—you don't even like me!'

'What's liking got to do with it?' and then he realised his mistake and was quick to catch her hand as she struck out at him. 'I didn't mean that . . . Jayne,' he tugged her hand, 'come and sit down . . .'

'No!' She snatched her hand away and turned towards the fire. What was she doing, allowing him to behave like that—actually responding to the damn man? He was on his feet and behind her, his hands on her shoulders were light until she struggled, and then they closed their grip fiercely.

'Listen to me.' He turned her round to face him, but she studied the rib of his sweater and refused to look into his face. She didn't want to be here so close—seeing him, feeling him, with her nerves still clamouring for satisfaction.

'Jayne.' He forced her chin up and stared down into her bright, defiant eyes. She had to fight this man, she just had to. She wasn't Jayne, she didn't behave like Jayne—she didn't approve of the promiscuous society, even if her friends had been laughing at her for years . . .

'Jayne,' he repeated firmly. 'Look, I was wrong . . .'

Joshua Brett wrong! He had her whole attention at last.

'I thought I could bring you over here—lock you up, beat you . . .'

'Thanks!'

'But it isn't going to work,' he continued, as if she hadn't interrupted.

'As long as you realise that, then there's nothing more to say,' Kelly retorted.

He gave her a little shake, his dark eyes mocking her. 'It isn't going to work because you don't bring out the fatherly instinct in me.' His expression was suddenly serious. 'Jayne . . .'

If he kept calling her that she would scream in a minute.

'Jayne,' he repeated. 'How long is it since that man in the divorce?'

She frowned, unsure of him. 'You mean, since I saw him?'

He nodded.

Jayne's affair had ended last summer. 'Six months,' she said quietly. 'Why?'

'And there's been no one else, since? No—permanent relationship?'

Suddenly Kelly knew what he was going to say—and

she couldn't believe it. Not like this ... not so cold-bloodedly ... 'There's been no one else,' she confirmed tightly.

He seemed pleased. 'Then I think it's about time we let our instincts have their way, don't you?' he said, almost pleasantly. 'I want you, Jayne, I want you badly. And from what I've just discovered, I know you want me too.'

Kelly was appalled that her own feelings were so transparent. She stared up at him, for once bereft of speech.

He smiled, and it was such a shattering, wicked, heart-stopping smile that it made her knees go weak.

'You're under my skin.' His hands gentled on her arms and slid all the way down to her wrists. 'You're a bewitching little minx; half woman, half child.' He silenced her protest with a finger against her lips. 'Now I know why all those older men wanted you. One moment you're ravishingly sophisticated and full of promises—and now, playing the little *ingénue*, you're enough to make a man want to eat you.'

'I thought you said maturity was more than the gratification of personal pleasure.' Kelly spat out the words. She had never, ever, been so humiliated in all her life. The man was an animal! How she could be attracted to him was quite incomprehensible.

Anger licked across his face, but he had it quickly under control. Everything about Joshua Brett spoke of icy nerves and iron control. Never would he be swept along on a grand passion of love. He saw a woman and he wanted her. But for how long? At the end of the affair she would be no less shattered than if she had been the real Jayne.

And that was what did it, that was what gave her the strength to look him in the eye and tell him very quietly to go to hell. She could see her sister in tears when a lover had deserted her. And no way was Kelly going to suffer an equal fate at the hands of this ruthless international businessman.

The fire crackled and the flames sent menacing

shadows leaping around the walls. And they were just standing there, staring at each other while the tension throbbed between them.

'Go to hell!' she repeated angrily. 'That's the only thing I've got to say to you.'

For one dreadful moment she thought he was going to hit her. The wind had got up and the trees outside moaned in the bitter darkness. If he didn't hit her he would throw her out there, and there were probably wolves . . .

'Your reaction is perfectly understandable in the circumstances,' he had the cheek to drawl. 'Naturally you're angry with me for dragging you away from all your friends. Of course you have to make a token protest . . .'

Her eyes widened in fury. 'It isn't a token protest. How dare you say that?' She felt a sudden overpowering urge to tell him the truth. She couldn't take much more of this mental torture. He only wanted her because he thought she was exciting and experienced—like Jayne. If she told him she was Kelly he would stop treating her like this. But was that what she really wanted?

He saw her indecision.

'What's the matter, Jayne? Changing your mind already?'

Jayne. Jayne. Always Jayne. Then she went suddenly pale. What was she doing even contemplating telling him who she really was? What punishment would Joshua Brett inflict when he found out she had been deceiving him from the very beginning?

'I'm sure it's a very interesting offer,' she managed to say, in what she hoped was the sort of voice he expected. 'But I told you before—love is important to me, and I'm certainly not prepared to play second fiddle to a man's career, however important that might be.'

He wasn't surprised, in fact she could almost believe he expected her to say that. 'Fair enough,' he shrugged, but there was nothing matter-of-fact in the cold, hard chill of his eyes. 'I simply thought we could have a nice cosy Christmas, that's all.'

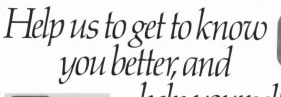

Help us to get to know you better, and help yourself to Melting Fire by Anne Mather.

Fill in and post this card today – no stamp needed

Anne Mather's classic romance 'Melting Fire' isn't generally available, but can be yours FREE when you complete and post the simple questionnaire overleaf.

Mills & Boon
Romance Survey

If you could spare a minute to answer a few simple questions about your romantic fiction reading, we'll send you in return a Free copy of 'Melting Fire' by Anne Mather.

The information you provide will help us to get to know you better, and give you more of what you want from your romance reading.

Don't forget to fill in your name and address – so we know where to send your Free Book!

see over ➜

Just answer these simple questions for your Free Book:

1. Who is your favourite romantic author?

_____

2. What was the last romance you read (apart from this one)? _____

3. How many books did you buy in the last month? _____

4. How did you hear about Mills & Boon? (Tick one:)
☐ Friend   ☐ Television   ☐ Magazines or newspapers
☐ Saw them in shops   ☐ Other (please describe) _____

_____

5. Please tick any of these book series that you have heard of:
☐ Silhouette Romances   ☐ Circle of Love   ☐ Candlelight
Ecstasy   ☐ Silhouette Special Editions ☐ Sapphire
Romances ☐ Pavanne Romances ☐ Nightshades
☐ Signature Collection

6. Where did you get this book? _____

7. Which age group are you in?   ☐ 16-20   ☐ 21-30
☐ 31-40   ☐ 40-45   ☐ 45+

8. After you have read your Mills & Boon novels, what do you do with them? (Tick box)
☐ Keep them   ☐ Give them away   ☐ Lend them to
friends   ☐ Other (Please describe) _____

9. What do you like about this book? _____

_____

Fill in your name and address, put this card in an envelope (you can fold it if you need to) and post today to:
Mills & Boon Reader Survey, FREEPOST, PO Box 236, Croydon CR9 9EL, Surrey.

NO STAMP NEEDED

Name _____

Address_____

_____

_____ Postcode _____

MFQ 1

'And afterwards?' she heard herself say.

He shrugged again. 'Who knows? All things are transient, especially relationships. That's something you must have found out pretty early on.'

She didn't know why, but something in his voice made her think of him and Glenda. How had he felt when that affair had come to an end?

'So what happens now?' she asked, instinct telling her that he would be bound to exact some terrible vengeance.

'We revert to my original plan.'

'Which is the beating and the locking up, I suppose.'

Joshua's eyes flashed dangerously. 'Stick around and you'll find out.'

CHAPTER SEVEN

'I DON'T have much option to do anything *but* stick around, do I?' Kelly responded, clattering the cups and saucers back on the tray. 'If you want some more tea you'll have to get it yourself. I want to unpack my bag. Which is my bedroom?'

Joshua laughed, a taunting, menacing laugh that made her heart sink. 'This is it.' He waved a large hand around the living room. 'I do use the loft in summer, but at this time of the year it's out of the question.'

'I'll manage.' They were both standing on the hearth-rug. The fire crackled between them.

'I *said* it's out of the question.' Joshua's voice warned her not to make trouble, but she was past caring now.

'You needn't think I'm sleeping down here with you just so that you can . . .'

'What?' he suggested angrily. 'So that I can take advantage of you?' He laughed harshly again. 'Don't kid yourself, Jayne. Suddenly I find that all desire for you has gone.'

She didn't believe him. He was lying. He did desire her—she knew that as well as if he had shouted it from the tallest tree. All her feminine intuition suddenly told Kelly that she had only to smile at him, to lift her little finger, and he would demonstrate his need for her in no uncertain manner . . .

She turned away quickly and heard him putting a few more logs on the fire. Nothing like this had ever happened to her before. Love, if that was what it was, seemed to be a strange mixture of vulnerability and power. Joshua had the power to hurt her deeply, yet now, maybe just for today, she had the devastating power to attract him. Never mind if he thought she was Jayne. She wasn't. She was Kelly. She looked down at her hand and stretched out long slim fingers. It was this flesh and blood that Joshua wanted, and all she had to do was turn round and walk over to him . . .

Kelly had never been so tempted in all her life. Joshua represented everything she hated, yet he really was the most lethally attractive man she had ever seen. Her breathing was unsteady and she had to close her eyes and count to ten . . .

'Jayne.' His dark brown voice finally broke through. 'You'd better look at these,' he said, when she turned round to face him. He was holding out a pile of forms and a small pocket book about birds. 'If you really can't cook, I'll get the supper while you go through these. It'll be a long day tomorrow; you'd better make sure you recognise the birds you see.'

She glared at him. 'Don't change the subject. I said I'm not sleeping down here. Now, will you show me how to get into the loft? I can see the trapdoor—presumably you do have a ladder.'

'Right. You want to see the loft—I'll show you.' He threw the papers on the coffee table and marched out to the back porch. An icy wind whistled round Kelly's legs when he opened the door—but it wouldn't be that cold up in the roof, would it? Didn't they say heat was supposed to rise?

If heat did rise, this cabin hadn't heard about it. Joshua brought the ladder inside and propped it up against the hatch. He went up first and slid it open, then he came back down again and waved Kelly upwards. 'There you go,' he offered. 'I'll bring up your bag.'

Kelly climbed up, but as she peered over the hatch, it was so cold up there that it felt as if an icy hand had gripped the top of her head. She didn't falter, she wouldn't give him the satisfaction, but when he climbed up behind her there was a satisfied smirk on his face.

'Cosy, isn't it? It's the chimney-breast, you see. Smoke from downstairs must raise the temperature by—oh, half a degree at least.'

She ignored him, and stared around the room instead. There was a bed, or at any rate a bed frame and spring.

Kelly presumed the mattress had been taken away for the winter. There was a skylight, as well, but it was covered with snow now. It was dark up here—creepy—and it was so cold that already her body was beginning to tremble.

'It must be six or seven below,' Joshua went on cheerfully. 'Of course, it'll drop a lot more in the night.' He was standing beside a pine wash-stand, his head was bowed to accommodate the low, sloping roof. It would be lovely up here in the heat of summer—but there was no way that anyone could sleep up here now.

'You've made your point,' said Kelly reluctantly, making for the trapdoor again.

'Satisfied?' He climbed back down after her and slammed the hatch shut.

Kelly had rushed over to the fire and was rubbing her arms to try and get them warm. 'I *said* you've made your point.'

'Good. Now *I'll* get supper—*you* read.'

Her teeth were still chattering. She hadn't imagined that anywhere could be so cold. Wouldn't it be better to be raped than die of exposure?

He didn't see her watching him as he walked across the room. Her eyes followed the tall, powerful figure with the lithe, narrow hips . . . Trouble was, it wouldn't be rape, would it?

Delicious aromas emanated from the kitchen as Kelly sat on the rug in front of the fire. She was supposed to be reading, but her mind was only half on the book. It all seemed pretty straightforward, really. There were lists of different birds down one side of the page, and you had to put a tick against each species every time you saw one, and also a tick against such things as habitat, whether the bird was airborne or resting, whether it was a year-round inhabitant or just a visitor. There was no way she was going to learn all the possible permutations in one evening. She didn't attempt it, so she tried to sort out her emotional feelings instead.

It wasn't easy because she didn't have any past experience to judge from. Oh, there had been several boy-friends, and there was Alan ... But he didn't mean anything to Kelly—none of the men in her life had ever meant anything to her beyond friendship.

And now there was Joshua. Joshua Brett, who suddenly stood in the way of her future peace of mind. Joshua Brett, who had touched her as if she belonged to him; who had made her want a man for the first time in her life. At nearly twenty, wasn't it time she found out what making love was all about? Wasn't this chance too good to be missed? Supposing she never felt like this for any other man again?

Kelly stared into the fire, the book on her lap forgotten. But what self-respecting woman wanted to act as a substitute? A substitute for Jayne, a substitute for all the women in Washington who didn't happen to be here right now. *'I just thought we could have a nice cosy Christmas, that's all.'* That was what Joshua had said, and it made Kelly's heart grow cold. He was the most sensually disturbing man she had ever met, yet that wasn't enough, even for a physical relationship. Didn't there have to be respect? And the only thing that Joshua felt for her, apart from physical attraction, was contempt.

'Has Glenda ever talked to you about her beauty farm?' asked Joshua. It was well after eight o'clock now, and they were eating supper off their laps. The fire was a bright blaze between them; the cabin warm and cosy, which accentuated the sound of the wind moaning in the frozen blackness outside.

'She was always talking to us about having one some day,' Kelly began carefully.

'Us?'

She felt trapped. 'The two of us,' and because she was forced to say it, she added, 'Kelly and me.' She watched him, almost holding her breath. *Kelly.* Let him say it—just once.

He didn't. He obviously wasn't interested. 'Did Glenda ever suggest that you might like to help her run it?'

Kelly stared at him in horror. Now what was she

supposed to say? Answer for herself, or answer for Jayne? Would Jayne be interested? It was a possibility that had never crossed either sister's mind.

'I—I'm not sure . . .' She felt the moisture break out all over her body. What had started out as a small-time deception seemed to be becoming immensely involved. *Oh, what a tangled web we weave . . .* she thought miserably. Everything was going wrong—surely he would find out the truth soon.

She chased the food around her plate, her throat suddenly dry. Supposing he found out now, here— tonight . . . The wind rose to a howl and whipped the fallen snow up against the window. Escape was impossible on a night like this . . . the cabin walls closed in, trapping her. Please don't let him find out, she prayed; but was anyone listening to her?

'Glenda never mentioned that she might need our help,' she tried again.

He picked up the word 'our'. 'Your sister's far too young—she has her education to finish. But I think it would be a good idea for you to take an active interest . . .'

Kelly's face set. Too young, was she? Right.

'It's out of the question,' she said firmly. 'I'm going home in January, and nothing is going to stop me. Not you—not your international empire—not if you tried to put me in a shuttle and launch me into space.'

Joshua almost laughed. 'I suppose that would be one way of keeping you out of trouble.'

'Yes,' she responded smartly, 'if it meant keeping me away from you. *You're* nothing but trouble, Joshua Brett. Glenda doesn't want me to work for her and you know it. She already has a partner, Al someone . . .' Kelly tried to remember what Glenda had told her on the phone.

'I know all about Mr Drury, and I'm not convinced that he'll make a suitable partner for your stepmother,' and although the words were quite casual, there was a certain tone in them that struck at Kelly's heart. He does still love her, she thought wretchedly, even after six years, even though his stubborn pride won't let him resume the affair. Yes, a man like Joshua Brett would have the devil's pride, and it was that pride that had trapped him in the ruthless pursuit of his career. Glenda had let him down at a time when he would have most needed her support. Was that why he had never fallen in love again? Now she began to understand the reason for his ruthless pursuit of women's bodies, but never the more intimate involvement with their minds. He didn't want to get involved—he didn't want to get hurt again . . .

A host of crazy ideas whirled around in her mind in unison with the windblown snow outside. She muttered something about clearing away the plates, then shot out into the kitchen. It was cold out there and she shivered.

It was absolutely ridiculous and she was a fool to contemplate such a preposterous idea . . . Kelly clung to the edge of the stainless sink and stared at the tightly drawn curtains. Then she pulled them back and gazed at the black, steamy window, watching ice crystals slide down the outside of the warm pane and slowly melt. That was how she felt; melting, wanting to warm him, wanting him to love again—to love her—to be loved in return . . . She wanted to show him that all women weren't like Glenda. They could be trusted . . .

Kelly swallowed and moved around restlessly. She put the kettle on and found some clean cups. Joshua was attracted to her, couldn't she use that attraction to make him fall in love with her? She clattered and banged about for several minutes, her whole body nervy, her fingers trembling, her heart leaping and dancing about all over the place. All she had to do was walk back in there . . . She took a deep breath and began moving forward . . . But she paused in the doorway from where she could see him sitting in the big leather armchair beside the fire. He had a file on his lap and was going through typewritten pages and making little notes in the margin. It wasn't anything to do with the bird-count. She sensed it was something about Glenda's prospective business— financial reports, or whatever.

She sighed, wanting to walk over and take the work out of his hands. She wanted to sit on the arm of his chair, maybe gently stroke his hair. She leant against the door jamb and closed her eyes for a second. She was out of her mind. She was Kelly—inexperienced, virginal Kelly. How far could she get before her inexperience would be obvious to him? And what right had she to imagine she could make him fall in love with her? But how would she know one way or the other, unless she tried to find out? Love was a dangerous game, this whole visit had been a dangerous game right from the beginning, so what difference did it make if she took one or two more chances?

'Coffee,' she said brightly, walking towards the fire and putting the tray down on the table. Joshua didn't look up from his work, but she wasn't disheartened— not yet. It was a pity she was only wearing these green cords and sweater. Even if they did accentuate her slim, shapely figure, they weren't quite the thing for an up-and-coming seductress.

'Do we have any liqueurs?' she tried again. 'I couldn't see any in the kitchen.'

This time she had his attention. The strong lines of his face stared up at her and she had a sudden urge to smooth all his tension away with the cool tips of her fingers.

'Over there.'

'I'll get it,' she said quickly, as he was about to get up. She found everything in a cupboard, there was a regiment of bottles; Joshua chose brandy and she had her favourite Cointreau. The bird book was still lying on the rug where she had left it, so she settled down there again, the flames highlighting her dark hair, her back only inches away from Joshua's outstretched legs.

He began reading his report again, or at least trying to. But he wasn't turning over any pages and she could feel his eyes burning into her back.

This was madness . . . 'What—er—time do we start tomorrow?' she began, turning round slowly to gaze up at him. His eyes were already on her—as she had known.

His coffee and brandy sat untouched on the table. Her heart was beating faster, her senses were heightened and she seemed aware of everything, yet everything moved in slow motion; almost as if the moves were pre-arranged.

'We leave about eight.' His rich dark voice had an unusual shake in it. 'We'll be out all day, so you'll have to stay pretty alert. We want a good count, there's no point in doing half a job.'

'Why count at all?' She had turned right round now and was resting her elbows on the arm of his chair. A slow, languorous mood was easing into her limbs. Firelight softened Joshua's features, they softened the firm outlines of chin and powerful shoulders. Yet the blurred edges didn't lessen his latent strength; if anything, it seemed to accentuate the smouldering, quiet virility of the man. Funny, she had never thought of him as a quiet man. But perhaps here in the mountains where he came to relax—perhaps here he found peace.

Firelight danced on his bright eyes and he half-closed them, looking down at her then through thick dark lashes. 'These hills were pretty badly treated, ecologically speaking,' he explained, 'right up to the first part of this century. The hill farmers had the devil's own job to scratch a living in the end, but by then the damage had been done. Fields burned off, trees felled, the soil reduced to worthless dust ... All that changed when they made it into a National Park. They've been trying to let nature have its way; trying to restore the balance. The wildlife's back, now that their habitat is restored ... But we have to find out what the balance is. Just who comes back, and who stays away ... and why. The only way to keep track is to come up here and count them.'

Kelly tried to listen to the meaning of his words, but it was only the rich timbre of his voice that held any attraction. His voice seemed to respond to some inner music of her mind ... it was as if their sound waves matched. It was crazy—but she didn't want to be sitting down here on the rug.

'I've been reading and reading,' she began, and noticed with surprise that her voice was husky. 'But there are so many different birds and I'm quite sure I'll never remember them all by tomorrow.' She picked up the book and offered it to him. 'Perhaps you could point out the ones I'm most likely to see.' Her large eyes were like liquid gold as she gazed up at him. She saw a muscle jerk in his cheek as he took the book from her. The fire crackled and spat and she noticed that the wind had dropped. She was noticing everything tonight . . . and then he was flicking over the pages quickly and her eyes were riveted to those strong, well-shaped hands.

She sat up on the arm of his chair and brushed against his shoulder.

'This little fellow is very prolific around here,' he said gruffly, and Kelly bent her head and purposely let her hair touch his face. He jerked away quickly, as if her touch had been fire, then he looked up and found her eyes on him, not the book—and a soft warmth spread to his cheeks as he muttered, 'You little witch.'

He waited for her, and slowly—very slowly—she bent her head and kissed him. It wasn't really a kiss, merely a brief touching of lips. She raised her head again, her pulses racing in spite of her calm exterior, and when he realised nothing more was coming, he opened his eyes.

'Do that again,' he ordered, and there was so much smouldering passion in his eyes, on his face, tangled up in his husky voice, that Kelly caught her breath.

The space between their lips gradually closed again, but this time, as the kiss began, Joshua wasn't taking any chances. He slid his hands possessively up her back, drawing her down on top of him.

The large leather chair creaked as its two occupants snaked together. Kelly was drowning—drowning. Everything was smooth and soft; warm and mellow. Joshua's hands were up and down her back; up and down. And now he was smoothing her hips and finding a sensitive little spot at the base of her spine.

She groaned softly and broke the kiss, not because she wanted it to end, but because she wanted to look at him; at the strong shape of his face, at the curve of dark brows and the sensuous, tantalising mouth. His body felt good beneath her; hard and exciting ... She kissed his chin and the tip of his nose and still he kept his eyes closed. There was no movement now, all was stillness and expectancy and an experienced man's willingness to wait.

And then she realised that he was allowing her to continue the initiative. *Her. Kelly* ... He didn't move, even his hands were still against her. Yet his breathing was a little ragged, she noticed, and his nostrils flared, like a proud stallion waiting.

Just for a second she was consumed with panic. What was she supposed to do? What key should she have held to what miracle? Joshua was an experienced man used to female companions who had learned the art of love-making before they met him. She kissed his cheek—and then the other one, just to give herself time to think, and when she smoothed the thick dark hair from his temple, he moaned and stirred restlessly beneath her and her body responded with an erotic lick of white-hot heat deep inside her.

Suddenly she wanted to kiss him passionately, to feed from the life-giving sweetness of those lips. But somehow she resisted, although she couldn't say why; and instead she planted the tiniest of tiny kisses all over his face.

Joshua allowed her to continue for maybe five minutes, and it was five minutes of the most exquisite discovery for Kelly. His hands began moving slowly again, the tempo of his breathing increased and the strain of his mounting desire was clearly etched in the sudden tautness of his face. With dissolving limbs and a euphoric haze, Kelly continued her ruthless torture. She kissed his closed eyelids, his nose, the lobe of each ear ... until his caressing hands were all over her back, thighs and bottom ... until his moan was continuous ... until she was aware with shattering clarity that his whole body was on fire for her.

'Enough!' His bright, burning eyes flew open and he

tangled his hands into her hair. This time she was forced
to kiss him fully on the mouth; now the passion broke
in both of them, and through it all Kelly's heart sang.
She could do it! It was easy—now all she had to do was
make him love her.

He was moving beneath her, his hands slipping beneath the rib of her sweater to slide smoothly across her
bare skin. His fingers traced tortuous trails down her
spine, then they slid around to her front and he found
the front fastening of her bra. With an expert flick he
released the catch and warm strong hands cupped both
her breasts.

Kelly was kneeling astride him, and the forced inti-
macy of his arousal, coupled with the searing caress of
her breasts, was drugging her into total compliance. She
arched her body and hung her head far back, her hair
falling in a dark cloud touched by firelight.

She clutched at his sweater, her fingers taut as she
sought for the hard muscle beneath.

'We've got too many clothes on,' he whispered, and
she was ready for him to stand up and carry her with
him.

They undressed each other slowly, kissing each new
discovery on the way. Kelly was floating in a blissful
haze. It couldn't really be happening, could it? It felt so
incredibly right, as if she had been waiting for this
moment all her life. There was no embarrassment, and
it amazed her, yet at the sight of Joshua's powerful
naked body, she had to admit that her excitement was
sharpened by an edge of primaeval fear. He was going to
make love to her and it was the only thing in the world
she wanted, yet she feared the unknown; she feared the
potent virility that she had wantonly unleashed.

They sank on to the rug together, fire shadows danced
over them. Joshua caressed and kissed her; her neck,
her breasts and all the slow, long way down to her toes.

'I want you badly,' he whispered, coming back up
and drawing away from her slightly.

Kelly gazed down the long length of him. 'I know,'
she whispered breathlessly, and suddenly she was shy,

knowing it was her turn to caress him. Her cool fingers brushed his hip and her large amber eyes gazed up at him uncertainly.

'Darling,' it was out before he could stop himself, 'how do you do it?' he muttered, his dark shadow finally covering her.

Her hands slid up and down his hard, smooth back. How good it felt . . . 'How do I do what?' Her eyes were magical now, she was a total woman for the first time in her life and she was loving every minute of it.

His eyes licked over her. 'How do you manage to look so innocent?' he whispered secretly. 'You must know how much it excites me, Jayne . . .'

Jayne? *Jayne!* The sky fell in. How could he possibly believe it? Didn't his instinct tell him she just *had* to be Kelly? Did he imagine she was putting on an act simply to please him? Couldn't he tell that every kiss and touch was given with love and genuine tenderness?

His knee smoothed the inside of her thigh . . .

'No!' She pushed against him. 'No, Joshua—don't! I don't want you.'

His face registered instant disbelief. 'Like hell you don't—anyway, it's too late now . . .'

Kelly screwed up her eyes in misery. Everything had gone wrong. What a fool she had been even to imagine that Joshua would think about love! They were struggling together now; her whole body screaming out for him, and there was nothing she could do to stop him. But he wouldn't be making love to her—he would be making love to some exciting image he possessed of her sister Jayne.

She jerked her head towards the fire and balled her fingers into tight fists. If he would only whisper her name, if he would only call her Kelly and kiss her, then the whole world would be put right—and she would be his for ever.

'Jayne, come on,' and then his touch of anger lifted. 'D'you want a fight? Is that it? Does it excite you? . . .' and suddenly he was all arms and legs, forcing her to submit to his aggressive possession. His hands tangled

into her hair again and brought her head round to face
him. Her protests were all part of the game now, the
dangerous game that she should never have begun. He
had cast aside his gentle mood; now his possession
would be unmerciful . . .

And then he stopped, his whole body went rigid and
she heard a muffled oath on his breath.

'Jayne.' He shook her. 'What's the matter? Answer
me. Why, in God's name, are you crying?'

She opened her eyes and saw the proud, tortured face
staring down at her. His eyes were like fire, his breathing
uneven, and the whole of his naked body rose above her
like a spectre.

'I—I just can't,' she sobbed, and two large tears
followed the path of those that had fallen a moment
before.

For one dreadful moment she thought he was going
to beat her—or rape her, but then he groaned and rolled
off her, to sit on the rug with his back to her; elbows on
knees, head in his hands. His spine was curved in tension, she could have counted the notches down its
length, and with all her being she wanted to reach out
and touch him and have him love her . . . But she
didn't—and he never would now . . .

With an enormous effort, Kelly scrambled into her
jeans and sweater before Joshua reached for his own
clothes. She didn't know what to do or say—and there
was this awful feeling of frustration mingling with the
pain.

Joshua began dressing, he was tucking in his shirt
now, and Kelly reluctantly raised her eyes to his face.

Their searing glance met and he made a quick grab
for her.

His fingers hurt, even through her sweater. His rage
was bubbling very close to the surface now. 'I ought to,'
he breathed, his eyes all over her, taking in her slim
young face without make-up, her loose unsophisticated
hair, her youthful body in simple clothes . . . his fingers
shook with the supreme effort of controlling himself.

Then his eyes hooded over, and, crazy thought, he

seemed almost uncertain. Then he suddenly thrust her from him and she toppled over on to the settee. 'Get out of my sight!' he roared. 'From now on keep out of my way.' He pointed a long finger at her. 'You won't get another chance. Lord knows why I'm giving you this one!'

'Great! That suits me fine.' Kelly struggled to her feet, all her love had gone, its place taken by cold, blinding hate. 'I can't think of anything I'd rather do than get out of your sight!' And without conscious thought she raced over to the back-porch door, pulled it open and charged straight out into the icy black and white night.

CHAPTER EIGHT

'Look, it's a bit difficult to explain, but I'm not Jayne—I'm Kelly.' As she raced out into the night, these were the words that raced with her.

Joshua chased after her and a flying rugby tackle had them both rolling over and over in the snow. Kelly was gasping. All the breath was knocked out of her—and with it her hate. She had to tell him the truth, and with that decision made, she spat out a mouthful of snow.

'What the hell did you do that for?' He dragged her up, brushing the snow off himself with one hand, and clinging on to her arm with the other. She stumbled and almost fell as he hauled her back towards the cabin.

'I know it sounds crazy,' she tried to form the words in her mind 'Jayne couldn't possibly come, so we decided—*I* decided—to come instead . . .' She loved Joshua and nothing was going to alter that now, and she couldn't stand this deception any longer. As they stumbled and slithered their way back down to the cabin she thought, 'I'm sorry, Glenda, if this messes up your plans. And I'm sorry, Jayne, if the London flat has to be sold . . .'

'Get inside.' He pushed her ahead, then came inside and slammed the door behind him. 'I suppose you think that was extremely funny.' He looked almost beside himself with rage. 'What good do you think pneumonia would do you?' his lips twisted nastily, 'or a broken neck?'

'With me out of the way think how peaceful it would be,' only it was difficult to speak because her teeth were beginning to chatter. The melting snow had soaked through her jumper. She rubbed her arms, but the circulation seemed to have gone to sleep.

He threw his sweater at her and for the first time she realised he had run after her in just his jeans and shirt.

'Go and take a hot shower and put that on.' He sounded as if he wished it could be her shroud.

'I'm perfectly all right—and I want to tell you something . . .'

'Don't argue—take a shower, or I'll do it for you!'

He would too. Kelly glared at him, then stalked off. Perhaps it wasn't quite the time to tell him she wasn't Jayne.

As the hot water drummed life back into her frozen bones, she tried to sort out exactly how she would tell Joshua. As she tried to think, she watched the little streams of water follow the shapely contours of her body, and suddenly there came a spasm of heat and longing as she recalled Joshua touching and caressing her in those very same places . . . Fool. If you hadn't been so uptight about him calling you Jayne, there wouldn't have been any need to run away and you could have been in there right now, lying beside him—making love . . . Kelly closed her eyes and chewed her full bottom lip. But you are uptight, and it has to be *you* he wants . . .

Eventually she came out of the shower wearing Joshua's sweater and very little else. Her jeans and sweater were really soaking and she had to hang them over the back of a chair and hope they would dry. His sweater came halfway down to her knees and the sleeves flopped over her hands by inches. She didn't look much like a Jayne-type seductress now—she looked young and silly, and she felt extremely foolish.

Joshua stared at her, tense with the supreme stupidity of all women everywhere. But as their eyes met the breath was suddenly knocked out of him and he expelled it on a long, weary note of disbelief.

'I have never, in all my life, met a woman half the equal of you.' He spoke slowly, the rich, well-modulated voice straining for his usual control. 'I have nothing but contempt for the person you've allowed yourself to become—and yet,' he broke off, his eyes all over her, 'and yet sometimes I could almost believe you're nothing more than an innocent child.'

Kelly, the real Kelly, was cut to the quick. Child, child—always a child. He'd have her back in nursery school next!

'Confusing, isn't it?' she snapped. 'But don't worry, you'll get over it.'

'Undoubtedly.' And he was all precise and cold again, and anything was better than that—even his hate. 'I'm going to take a shower now—after that, bed.'

As he spoke, Kelly looked past him and noticed that while she had been in the shower he had assembled the settee into a double bed. There were two single sleeping bags snuggling side by side. So much for telling her to keep out of his way! 'I'm not sleeping there—and that's final!'

'Sleep where you damn well please.' He picked up a sleeping bag and cushion and threw them at her. 'Out on the porch—up in the loft—but I *suggest* that you stay as near as possible to the fire.'

Kelly clutched her soft, floppy armful and glared at him. Why did she have to go and fall in love with such an unfeeling brute? 'I'm perfectly capable of finding somewhere for myself,' she said loftily, and he muttered something, probably very rude, as he strode past her.

'And a Merry Christmas to you too,' she mumbled to herself.

He turned back sharply. 'What?'

'Nothing.' And to her relief, he went.

She found a spot over by the window that was slightly screened from the fire by the table and chairs. It gave her a bit of privacy, but not much. She snuggled into the bag and pulled the zip right up. It was hard on the floor and pretty chilly over here. She felt cross and humiliated, and she *had* meant to tell Joshua the truth. Only when he was in this mood it would have been suicide.

The shower stopped and she held her breath—waiting. She snuggled down deeper, eyes tight shut. He came back in and she heard him put a couple of logs on the fire, switch off the last table lamp and lastly ease himself into bed.

Kelly didn't move, not a muscle—and Joshua didn't say goodnight.

The reign of silence continued the following morning. Joshua woke Kelly with a shake, making no comment that she was now curled into a tight ball on the rug.

She rubbed her eyes and grunted. Now that it was time to get up she was actually warm. It had been the coldest night of her life, and in desperation she had crept over to the fire and put her sleeping bag right next to the hearth. Joshua hadn't woken, at least not then, but he must have got up a couple of times and stepped over her, because the fire was still alight and the pile of logs had diminished.

They showered, dressed and tidied up as if a mutual disarmament pact had been signed. They both stalked the tiny cabin deliberately keeping out of each other's way. Joshua made her make a pile of sandwiches and fill two flasks, one with soup, one with coffee. And Kelly didn't argue, she just stood in the cupboard of a kitchen and kept busy, because it wasn't eight o'clock yet; far too early to shatter the peace. There would be plenty of time for that later on.

'Ready?' The stern voice broke in on her thoughts.

'Almost,' she called back. Yes, she was almost ready to tell him who she really was.

He packed their lunch in a rucksack, then shrugged himself into his sheepskin jacket. It suited him; he had the height and rugged toughness to carry it off. Kelly's heart suddenly ached for him, but she bit her lip and turned away.

'You ought to wear a hat,' he said, as she was slipping on her gloves.

'I've already told you, I don't wear one,' and for a moment he looked almost indecisive.

'Come on then,' he added sharply, opening the front door and letting in the cold air.

Kelly sighed irritably and picked up the clipboards, pencils and binoculars he had put ready for her. Heaven knew how this bird-count project would work out. One thing was certain, this was going to be the craziest Christmas Eve she had ever spent.

But all her anger vanished as she marched out to the front porch. Brilliant, early morning sun shone down from the bluest sky she had ever seen. But it hadn't raised the sub-zero temperature, instead it had somehow waved a magical, crystal wand over all the Blue Ridge Mountains. Only they weren't blue now, but had been transformed into a glittering, sparkling fairyland. Kelly had seen hoar-frost at home when every tree, twig, branch and hedgerow was covered with furry whiteness. But this was totally different. At some time in the night everything must have been covered with moisture, and now it was frozen—frozen in a coat of clear ice. Now, every tree trunk, every branch, twig and bush shone as if it had been made of glass, and sunbeams bounced back from it all like diamonds.

'Mind the steps—they're treacherous.' But even Joshua's voice calling up couldn't dispel her sense of wonder.

Imagine being able to see all this, not because you were wealthy or famous or could buy it—but just because the miracle that had brought you here had coincided with one of nature's miracles.

The steps and handrail were icy and Kelly picked her way down with great care. Joshua had the car running and he was de-icing the windscreen.

'It's beautiful,' she muttered, still in a bit of a daze.

'Yes.' His voice was tense and his eyes quickly slid away from her face 'We call it an ice storm.'

They climbed into the car together and fastened their seat-belts. Ice storm. That just about sums up this whole business, thought Kelly, as the car inched its way out on to the track. Ice was a sure good way to describe Joshua Brett; icy and remote, keeping a cold distance between them, as he was again now. But how many times had a storm of passion broken through his cool reserve? Ice storm! She shivered, and for a moment the brilliant, sparkling morning mocked her.

They didn't speak in the car. The track was narrow

and twisted upwards, and they finally reached the clear
road at the top by a combination of snow-tyres and
Joshua's driving skill. Kelly expelled her breath with
relief. It couldn't have snowed in the night, the Skyline
Drive was smooth, dry tarmac, and they headed south
for four or five miles. Joshua had told her that everyone
was meeting at a Ranger station. Kelly began to wonder
who 'everyone' was.

Whoever they were, Joshua seemed to know them all.
Kelly climbed out of the car and was surrounded by
cheery faces, bright anoraks and businesslike walking
boots.

'This is Jayne Osborn, she's staying for Christmas . . .'
Joshua's unwitting lie bounced back at Kelly, sharply
cutting as the cold, clear air. Then the maps were
brought out and everyone was told the area that had
been allotted to them. There were one or two queries
and then everyone was walking back to their cars.

It was a relief to be away from those speculative eyes.
Kelly wouldn't have minded people thinking she was
having an affair with Joshua if it had been true. But it
wouldn't be now—not after he knew the truth . . .

Two other cars followed Joshua to the same parking
area, and for a dreadful moment Kelly thought they
were going to have company. There were a couple of
women in the group of part-time ornithologists; one
looked young and inquisitive and the other looked as if
she would like to know Joshua much better. His eyes
had smiled at her back at the Ranger station. The last
thing Kelly wanted was to spend a day wandering
around after the two of them.

But it didn't happen. After a brief discussion, they
split into three groups; Joshua and Kelly headed towards a narrow trail going south. She turned her jacket
collar up to protect her ears a bit. It was very cold; this
side of the ridge was still in shadow. The binoculars
bounced against her chest as she plodded after Joshua
and her sense of humour returned in spite of everything.
*I must be mad, traipsing over a mountain to count birds
in the freezing cold! He's very lucky I'm Kelly and not*

Jayne . . . And with that she began to giggle.

'We wish you a Merry Christmas,' she began singing, but Joshua stopped in his tracks suddenly, shushed her, and raised his heavy fieldglasses to his eyes.

'Chickadees—five; three male, two female,' he said, and Kelly looked up into the trees instead of writing it down. Operation Bird Count had begun!

They kept moving all morning, until the sun crept round to them and then the trees sparkled again and everything shone in icy magic. They stopped for some coffee and a family of little black and white nuthatches chattered above them in the trees.

'Not their usual perky selves,' said Joshua, gazing upwards.

'Why?'

'It's the ice—it's sealed in their food supply of insects and things.' He shook out his empty mug and screwed it back on the flask. Kelly did the same, and then followed him down the track again. So the ice storm wasn't doing the birds any good either. It was still a beautiful, glittering day, but now she hoped it wouldn't go on for too long.

It was sheltered in the wood, almost warm, as the count went on, and Kelly filled column after column of information. She gradually realised that all the tension had gone. This couldn't have been more different from the glitter of Washington, but she realised that this was the nearest she would get to the feel of the real America. America had been built by the toughness of people like the ones who had once lived in these mountains. Down below on the plain, which was out of sight now, the Indians and buffalo had reigned. Up here, with the birds and trees and the clearest air she had ever breathed, up here you could feel just a tiny, tiny part of belonging to it all. Now she knew why Joshua came.

And along with this feeling of rightness, of feeling suddenly at one with everything, Kelly knew that her love for Joshua was right and true—and as natural as these magnificent mountains. She smiled to herself and stared at his broad back as they followed the narrow

trail. The day wasn't working out as he had intended.
She was supposed to be hating this, instead it was turning into the most perfect day of her life. Her pulses
quickened. It was the kind of day when anything could
happen.

They had lunch beside the tumbled, gnarled ice of a
frozen waterfall. They ate their sandwiches as chickadees, nuthatches and titmice gathered in the trees
nearby. Kelly could tell the difference now; as she scrib-
bled away she could feel Joshua's dark eyes on her.

'There's another one,' he said, after a few moments;
the rest of the flock had scattered at a sudden warning
noise.

Kelly shook her head and when he looked surprised,
she explained, 'We've already counted him. See,' she
pointed, 'he's got a little white feather sticking out at a
funny angle.' It flew away as she spoke—but Joshua
kept staring into the tree for a long time. His profile
was stern and unfathomable; Kelly's heart ached for
him.

They were following a grid pattern, back and forth,
covering a large section of the hill. Now Kelly judged
that they were heading roughly back towards the car. It
was three-thirty, they had probably another hour still to
walk, and she guessed you didn't stay out in the Blue
Ridge Mountains once the sun had gone down.

There was a sudden thrashing in the undergrowth
ahead, and they both stopped instantly as something
took off. The bird was large, low and heavy, like a tubby
cargo plane amidst the chickadee and nuthatches' tiny
executive jets.

'Any idea?' Joshua questioned.

Kelly shrugged. 'A fat pheasant?' and his eyes smiled.
His eyes smiled!

'Not bad. A grouse, a ruffed grouse, to be precise,'
and her fingers shook as she wrote it down. The sun
was sneaking through the bare trees—it had gone down
a long way. She shivered.

'Cold?'

They stared at each other and she nodded. Nobody

spoke. Nobody moved. It was as if they didn't want to leave this place, as if they wanted to remember it for ever . . .

He smiled again, gently, tenderly, with warm liquid eyes and suddenly the day slid away from them. The glittering ice storm, the birdsong, the brilliant blue above and the firm white snow beneath their feet, it all melted, blurred around the edges of their vision, until they only saw each other, could only hear each other breathing . . . The world became just the two of them without beginning or end.

Joshua's expression intensified and she knew he could see all the way down to her soul. There was warmth and passion there, and it both surprised and delighted him.

Kelly held her breath; she mustn't rush anything—he had to find out for himself . . . The clipboard and pen dropped from her hand and neither of them noticed. Her heart was beating fast now, drumming in her ears, shouting at her to do something . . . say something. Everything about her was alive and tingling . . . and he knew, he knew now, she was sure of it. And then the space between them had disappeared. He was all arms and strength holding her, kissing her. His lips were cold, but his mouth was warm. They clung to each other, marvelling at this instinctive coming together. It was timeless, never-ending . . . but slowly it did end. The world crept back, Joshua was frowning and Kelly was wincing at the pain in her chest.

'Damn binoculars!' and then he was laughing, they were both laughing because they had too many clothes on and they couldn't get to each other, and it was late anyway, and if they didn't get back soon they would freeze to death. She clutched hopefully at his thick sheepskin jacket, but it was pointless. 'Come on—home, quickly,' he said, turning up her collar and kissing the end of her nose. But she wouldn't let him go—not yet.

'Joshua.' She coiled her arms around his neck again. 'I have enjoyed today—really.'

He still looked a bit bemused. 'I know.' Then he put

her purposely from him. 'I said home, my girl.' He was studying her carefully. 'What I really meant was—bed.'

'Yes,' she whispered up at him.

He covered both her hands with his own; they felt strong and firm, but there was a slight tremor in them. 'No more crying,' he said softly.

'No.'

'Promise.'

'Yes.' And it was a promise, because everything had changed now. There was something special and deep between them—a trust. It was a young, fledgling trust, but it was there nevertheless. Kelly knew she would spend the rest of her life nurturing it with love.

The shadows were long when they reached the car, and although the sun was still visible across the Shenandoah Valley, there was no warmth in it now. It was bitterly cold on the outside, but Kelly still glowed on the inside from the heat of Joshua's love.

He hadn't said he loved her—but that would come.

They tumbled into the car and kissed again.

'You're adorable,' Joshua whispered. Adorable? Well, that was something. He started the engine, his eyes still on her face. It wouldn't be long now and they could be really together . . .

Only when they got back to the Ranger's house to hand in their papers, everyone was inside having hot drinks and recounting the day's events. They were dragged into it, everyone was laughing and chatting, and the blonde ornithologist flirted with Joshua, but he hardly noticed anyone but herself. He stayed close, touching Kelly frequently, and she suddenly realised that he was already making love to her. She could feel every pore in her body respond with a mixture of excitement and weakness. Her palms were damp. How on earth could he do it? Wasn't everyone in the room aware of it too? But they weren't, and having arranged to meet them all again the day after tomorrow, Joshua and Kelly finally escaped.

This time they ran to the car, fell into it and roared towards the road. But before they reached it, Joshua slammed on the brakes and the big station wagon slid to a halt.

'Put your seat-belt on,' he said, taking a deep, steadying breath, and they both fought to calm themselves—they weren't home yet.

He kept to the speed limit, yet Kelly ached for him to go faster. Twilight was setting in fast, there were little lights twinkling up from the grey valley; the sun had gone now—only a few high clouds still carried a tinge of pink, as if they were unwilling to say goodbye to the day.

Five miles of twisting Skyline Drive before they reached the track. Five miles to savour the sweetness to come—to wonder at the miracle that had brought them together.

Kelly twisted round in her seat and gazed at him. He glanced at her quickly, then turned his attention to the road again, but there was a smile on his lips. It was wonderful to look at him openly, there would be no more peeping at Joshua Brett beneath her lashes . . .

Joshua Brett. *The* Joshua Brett. She watched his hands manipulating the steering wheel as they rounded another tight corner. Joshua Brett of Space Design U.K. The international businessman who knew all the right people on both sides of the Atlantic, who had a beautiful house in Washington—who chose his friends from distinguished circles . . . This was the man who loved her. Funny, but today she had forgotten all about the glamour.

A touch of fear intruded into her happiness. Today, the man who had fallen in love with her was the Joshua Brett who walked hillsides counting birds. Were his two lives totally separate? Did he see her as fitting into only this particular scene?

Nonsense. Her self-confidence returned. There was only one Joshua Brett, even if he did live two lives. Only one man capable of loving her. She would just have to get used to the many-faceted side of his existence.

They were home. The track was extremely icy, but he managed it with care, then they were easing into the layby beneath the cabin. They climbed up the steps to-gether, arms around each other, and Kelly was amazed at the difference in mood from when they had left that morning.

It was cold inside, and for a moment they stood there, almost selfconsciously; Kelly didn't know quite where to look or what to say.

Joshua dumped the gear on the table and smiled at her. 'You get a hot drink—I'll light the fire, and then we'll go to bed.'

Excitement, pleasure, fear—all stabbed at her to-gether. 'What—what about supper?' she heard herself say.

'We'll see about that—later.' The rich chord of music he called his voice played havoc with her nerve ends.

She fled to the kitchen and put the kettle on. Panic followed her.

'What's the matter with you?' she began to mutter. 'It's what you want, isn't it? You can't stay a rotten silly virgin for ever—and it has to be Joshua—it *has* to be!'

Her mind, her capacity for coherent thought, went squidgy at the edges. She found the mugs and the coffee, while her panic danced around the tiny space telling her to run, one moment, then laughing at her from another direction, and telling her to stay . . .

The fire was beginning to crackle and she heard the settee being unfolded. Her palms went damp again. Lord, she couldn't—she was scared—*scared*? Fool. Imbecile. Somehow she found the tin with the fruit cake in it, only the lid was stuck . . .

'Never mind that.' All at once Joshua was behind her, his arms wrapping her to him, his teeth gently pulling at her ear.

'I thought you might be hungry . . .' she began.

'I am.' He turned her around. 'But who said anything about food?' He kissed her and she started drifting down a long, soft tunnel. 'Come on, never mind all this,' and the coffee was forgotten as he picked her up and carried her into the living room. It was still cold in there; the fire was spitting and crackling as he put her down gently;

and there was the couch, all unfolded and snug with sleeping bags zipped together.

'I've been thinking,' Kelly muttered through a tight throat. 'I—I haven't got you a Christmas present,' but even as she said it she realised it wouldn't make him go off her.

Joshua's fingers slid under her sweater and smoothed the soft bare skin beneath. 'I wouldn't say that,' he whispered, drawing her even closer. 'I'd say you were the nicest Christmas present I've ever had.'

'Really!' Big, innocent, sherry-coloured eyes gazed up at him and for a moment he seemed to hesitate. The stern lines of his face were softened, yet somehow solemn, and his eyes were all over her face, as if he was drawing up her most secret soul for his inspection.

Secrets! *Jayne!* But the time for talking had passed— and it didn't matter now. Tomorrow she would tell him. They would wake up together and it would be all warm and beautiful . . . and they would laugh about it and he would say he didn't care what she called herself. He would say that he loved her—Kelly . . . Kelly, Kelly, Kelly. She imagined the sound of her name on his lips. If only he would say it now!

'*Of course* you're the nicest Christmas present I've ever had.' Then he frowned. 'Mind you, there was a puppy I had once . . .'

'Beast!' And then they were laughing and fighting and they both fell on the sofa in a tangle of arms and legs.

Then there was a sudden stillness. The laughing stopped and a slow beat of mutual desire throbbed between them.

Kelly touched his cheek with a gentle finger. 'I love you,' she whispered up at him, and he closed his eyes, savouring the moment, although his face remained taut and enigmatic.

There was no panic this time. They kissed; slowly, sensuously, the rhythm of their bodies an ancient language far sweeter than any words.

'I want you,' Kelly whispered, while her fingers tangled into his thick dark hair, drawing his face down to her bare midriff.

'Shh!' He claimed her lips and kissed her to silence. 'Not yet—have patience, my love ...' and it went on and on, the movement, the deep warm heat melting her bones, blurring her edges so she couldn't have said where she ended and Joshua began.

At long, long last, when he judged the time to be right, he undressed her. But even then the torture continued, because he did it, oh, so slowly, and as each item fell to the floor, he kissed the warm, bare flesh beneath.

Kelly's mind had long since given up its existence to Joshua. He was the whole world, the beginning, middle and end of life itself. How was it possible for one man—only *this* man—to rouse her to so much deep love and desire?

And then it was his turn to get undressed. She tried to help, but the shirt buttons were back to front and his belt buckle was stiff. Her hands were shaking so much anyway, so he laughed and stripped himself, while Kelly lay back in the warm softness and watched him.

And just for a moment it was as if she was outside herself, looking down on both of them. There she was, lying naked, and there was Joshua, firelight licking over the hard contours of his magnificent body ... and she waited for the heat to come to her cheeks—where was the embarrassment, the shame? Nowhere. And this time she knew she wouldn't push him away because now there was trust and understanding on both sides. It was enough.

Joshua sat on the edge of the settee for one final moment, allowing himself the infinite pleasure of gazing down at the long, curvaceous length of her. Then he picked up her hand and kissed her wrist, then the inside of her elbow ... And then he was there, his dark shadow covering her, and she gasped at the special exquisiteness that can only be bare skin next to bare skin.

'Joshua, please . . .' she began desperately.

'I know, darling,' he groaned softly as her hand slid down his back and thighs. 'Jayne, don't, I'm trying to hang on . . . I think you want me to be slow and gentle this time . . .'

She closed her mind to his obvious mistake. 'I don't want you to hang on,' she said, even now not knowing quite what she was inviting.

A tremor ran through him and beneath the smooth hard skin she felt his muscles tighten in aggressive anti-cipation. She caught her breath, fearful of the unknown, suddenly aware of the frightening power of this man. Now she sensed he was losing the grip on his control. Her words had given him the excuse to do—to do what?

Only this time panic didn't stay. This time her body overruled all else and she found herself responding to Joshua's urgency with a passionate will of her own. The deep red heat that had been her whole body was now a white hot flame concentrated in one intimate spot.

'Joshua . . .' His name was expelled on a breath of agony.

'I know.' His voice was tight. 'I can't wait any more, either.' His eyes were all over her, torturing himself, savouring every inch of her until the very last moment. His breathing was ragged, then he closed his eyes in self-inflicted agony. 'Jayne. My darling Jayne, what have you done to me?'

Kelly basked in his love. No man had ever looked at her like that. No man's voice had ever trembled with so much emotion.

She folded him against her. It was suddenly still and calm, like the eye of the hurricane. His magical, caress-ing hands were moving away. Instinct made her shift her body slightly . . . Everything was all right, this was how it was meant to be . . .

He lifted her towards him.

'I adore you,' he muttered helplessly.

She smiled a safe, secret smile. 'I know.'

'You won't go back to England, will you?'

Her heart leapt. He came even closer. 'Not if you don't want me to.'

'Jayne, Jayne . . .'

She smiled again and smoothed his hair. 'Hush,' she whispered, 'don't call me that . . .'

They kissed and it was long and beautiful, and now they would finally be one. Joshua drew slowly away and Kelly held her breath, knowing that the time had come . . . Only nothing happened. Did he have to torment her for ever? Then she gradually opened her eyes to find him gazing down at her in puzzlement.

'What do you mean?' His voice was still quiet with no message of its own.

'Mean what?' She was in a state of bliss and nothing else could penetrate.

'You said,' he blinked a couple of times, 'you said—don't call you Jayne.'

'I didn't mean any . . .' 'anything' couldn't quite make itself heard.

'Yes, you did.' He gently pulled a strand of hair off her face. 'Why?' He was curious, nothing more, gazing down at her slim young figure and dark, straight hair, the hair she was always winding behind her ears . . . the girl he had known since her schooldays . . .

The small dark cabin was warm and cosy—watching them. For a long time they didn't move—couldn't speak. Joshua was trying to make sense out of the encroaching madness. Kelly could see his mind working, could sense everything was falling away . . . and she willed it, *willed* it, to stay here for ever.

He traced a line down her face, then picked up a handful of her hair and let it slip slowly through his fingers. Yet he wasn't really seeing her, he was looking way back down the years, seeing Stuart Osborn with his two daughters . . . And now he was looking back at the past few days . . . and she saw the truth dawn on him slowly. He tried to dismiss it at first, but as the colour drained from his face she knew that everything had become crystal clear. *Everything!*

'Joshua—it doesn't matter . . .'

'Doesn't matter?' His eyes crackled with hatred. 'You can lie there and say it doesn't matter!' Rage burst out of him with a violence that made her tremble. 'You

didn't want me to call you Jayne because you're not
Jayne, are you? For God's sake don't lie to me this
time.' He shook her. 'Tell me, damn you! You're not
Jayne.' Then he laughed bitterly. 'Which means you've
got to be sweet baby sister Kelly.'

Kelly! He had said it. But there was no joy in victory,
nothing she could do but acknowledge it. But her tearful
mumble didn't satisfy him.

'Say it so I can hear it,' he grated.

'I said you're right.' A tear slid down her cheek and
she chewed her bottom lip. 'You're right—I am Kelly.'

In the silence that followed she knew she had lost
Joshua for ever.

CHAPTER NINE

'WHY?' Anger forced out the word, then Joshua immediately regretted it. 'No, don't answer that. I don't think I want to know . . .' He dropped her back on to the cushions as if she had been burning his fingers. Then he swung his feet to the floor and sat with his back to her; elbows on knees, face resting in his hands. On any other man it would have been an attitude of exhaustion, but not for Joshua Brett. Rage beat out of him, the long column of his spine was taut, thigh and biceps bunched in an agony of aching muscle. Kelly could tell he was forcing his breathing to be deep and steady. Why was he so cross? What was so dreadful? Surely if he loved her . . .

She reached out to him. 'Joshua——' she began uncertainly.

'Don't *touch* me!' His voice shook with emotion. It frightened her, it didn't sound like him at all. Then his control finally broke, as if the touch of her fingers had severed a tenuous cord. He rounded on her, anger and bitterness transforming his face almost beyond recognition. 'Have you the slightest idea of what you were doing?' he shouted. 'Do you know what nearly happened? What I could have done to you? . . .'

Kelly flattened herself into the cushions; there was nowhere she could escape . . . and in a minute he would hit her. 'I—I don't know what you mean. I wasn't trying to do anything.'

· 'Ha!' He threw back his head, but the laugh was brief and mirthless. 'Then let me tell you,' he grated, and before she realised what was happening he had dragged her up in front of him. Her hair was everywhere and as she tossed it out of her eyes it swung across her bare shoulders. Joshua's eyes flashed, and even through her panic she realised that he still liked what he saw. 'Little baby sister was trying to grow up in one easy lesson, wasn't she? Jealous of Jayne, were you?' She tried to hit him, but he ducked. 'Thought you'd cash in on her reputation?'

'Don't you dare speak to me like that!' Kelly struggled, her teeth clenched and her face twisted in an effort to force herself free. But it was useless, he had no intention of letting her go. And beneath the fear and anger came the quick beat of excitement as bare limbs tangled together.

Joshua felt it too, and with a mighty effort he pushed her away. 'Have you ever actually been in a man's bed before?' but all she could do was stare at him in horror. This had to be the very worst thing he had ever said to her. 'Answer me—have you?' and there was no love or even desire in his eyes; just a deep, burning hate.

'No,' she mumbled, managing to cover herself at last with a corner of the sleeping bag.

Savage hands ripped it away and his eyes abused her. 'Have you any idea what I could have done to you? I thought you were—were an experienced woman.' He paused and passed an unsteady hand over his face. 'I could have put you off men for life—*understand me*? In fact, I've a good mind . . .'

'Don't touch me!' She scrabbled back across the settee. This wasn't the Joshua she knew. There was so much violent aggression, she could feel it pulsating round the tiny cabin, bouncing back from the walls; electrifying, suffocating . . . They stared at each other while the maelstrom whirled around them. Kelly knew that now anything could happen. Joshua could hit her or rape her and there was nothing she could do about it . . . and he looked like a man dragged to the every edge of his endurance. Round and round, spinning in a tighter and tighter circle towards destruction . . . She closed her eyes and waited, holding her breath, so weak with emotion that she couldn't even raise her hands in defence.

'I wish to God I'd never set eyes on you.' Joshua's voice was cold and level and totally without emotion.

Kelly opened her eyes and stared at him. Everything was suddenly shrouded in a great stillness. There was no wind outside, no night noises. The fire didn't crackle and the cabin walls didn't creak. Joshua's battle had been fought—and he had won. There would be no hitting—no raping. The heat had gone out of his rage. He was in control again; that cold icy control that she knew so well.

'Joshua.' For the second time she tried to begin some sort of explanation.

'No.' He turned away from her and began putting on his clothes. 'I don't want to hear another word.'

'But you don't understand,' she persisted.

He paused in the act of doing up his belt. 'Oh, I understand all right. I understand that you've taken me for the biggest ride ... When I think of the fun you must have had ...'

Fun! She was shocked to silence, watching as he put on the last of his clothes with a certain methodical automation; socks, shoes, thick cream sweater. Then he reached for his sheepskin jacket and she finally realised what he was doing.

'You can't!' She sat up quickly, bringing the sleeping bag with her, but past caring now if she was naked or not. 'Joshua, no—it's late—the track's dangerous—there's nowhere for you to go ...'

'And there's no reason to stay here.'

Kelly went cold all over. So cold that as he went out she didn't feel the bitter night air as it rushed to fill warm corners.

She stood on the hearthrug, naked and completely motionless. The sleeping bag still held in one lifeless hand, the dying fire highlighting her soft round figure. An artist would have painted the scene and called it *Solitude*. Somewhere in the back of her mind she heard the car's engine cough into life. Joshua wasn't here any more ... a long time passed and she didn't move.

Eventually she shivered and automatically wrapped the sleeping bag around herself, sinking down on the rug, crosslegged, squaw-like, then the words came—and questions. Yet the threads of her thoughts were still tangled.

He's gone . . .

Ought to put some logs on the fire . . .

Why? . . .

Because he doesn't love me . . .

It didn't hurt—not yet. There was just a great numbness. She was very tired, so that when she crawled over to the log basket her movements were slow and heavy, as if she had suddenly grown old.

Joshua had gone. His car would skid off the road—he would be killed and they would never see each other again . . .

It was seven o'clock. No—surely . . . but her watch hadn't stopped. Seven o'clock. Was that all?

Seven o'clock, eight o'clock, nine . . . At nine o'clock the pain started and the first tear slid down Kelly's face.

She felt better after a good cry. It didn't solve anything, but it changed the hurt into a washed-out weariness, which by comparison was a relief.

Joshua was a good driver—he wouldn't really be killed. She dressed slowly; it was getting on for ten, he had been gone three hours. If the main roads were clear he could be back in Washington by now. She pulled her sweater on, then groped under the settee for her shoes. She could just picture him arriving home, picking up the phone . . . 'My plans have changed,' he would be saying. To whom? . . . Easy. The brunette from the Embassy—and if she was busy there would be little what's-her-name from next door. Really, he shouldn't encourage such an adolescent infatuation. Rosey, that was her name—and she probably had a mother who was equally besotted with Joshua. He would go to a party tonight, and be invited to spend Christmas with half of Washington, no doubt . . .

Kelly made some fresh coffee, sorted out the fire again and tried to decide what happened next. There was so much food and so many logs that she could stay up here for ages . . . Or she could trek up to the Ranger's house and beg a lift into Luray. Surely there would be a bus back to Washington? Only then what? Walk into Joshua's house, where he didn't want her, asking for the fare money home?

And then she remembered all the other problems. Jayne. Would Joshua demand that she leave the Seychelles and come to Washington? And would he be so angry that he would refuse Glenda her loan? So there went the London flat . . . Oh, hell!

Eleven o'clock . . . twelve. It was Christmas Day. She decided to open a bottle of wine and get drunk.

She was halfway through her second glass when she heard a car coming down the track. She held the glass against the fire and peered at it. Must be powerful stuff—she was hearing things now . . . Silence—she relaxed again, but suddenly there were footsteps on the porch and the cabin door was thrust open.

Kelly leapt to her feet. 'You!'

'Who were you expecting? Father Christmas?'

She smiled thinly, reluctantly acknowledging his little joke. There was snow on his jacket, on his hair, and on his long curly lashes. As he came across the room she could smell whisky, yet there was nothing in his movement to suggest it.

Her lips curled with contempt. 'You've been drinking,' she said, swaying slightly.

His dark eyes looked from her to the tilting glass in her hand, and then onward to the bottle on the hearth that was still more than half full. 'Exactly how long is it since you've eaten?' and some tiny part of her registered that his former rage had now turned to exasperation.

Food? It was a good question, and while she stood on the rug and thought about it, Joshua went into the kitchen and started banging about.

A toasted cheese sandwich and a large piece of fruit cake were soon put on the coffee table. Joshua took her glass and pushed her down on to the settee.

'Lunch time,' she declared suddenly. 'That's when I last ate. In the snow—by a frozen waterfall.' Only she didn't want to remember the glorious time that had been yesterday. Neither did Joshua. He just sat down in the armchair and told her to eat.

Food, warmth, wine and the strain of the evening caught up with Kelly in a rush. She didn't know why Joshua was here—but she would think about that tomorrow.

'I just think I'll have a little lie down,' she said, her eyelids drooping heavily, and as she keeled over across the settee she was asleep before her head touched the cushions.

Joshua didn't undress her—he didn't even touch her; just covered her with both sleeping bags, replenishing the fire, then settled back in the solitary discomfort of his chair.

Kelly woke up quickly in the morning and everything came back to her in a rush. She struggled on to one elbow, fighting with covers; her clothes were tight and twisted and she felt as refreshed as a piece of old chewed-up string.

She could hear Joshua moving about on the back porch, so she took the opportunity to stagger out of bed, grab her brightly coloured nylon roll-bag and make a dash for the shower room.

When she eventually emerged nearly half an hour later she felt only slightly better. She smelt of soap and shampoo, her hair was squeaky clean, her skin glowed from being attacked by a loofah and she had a complete change of clothes. Although there was no need for her to pretend to be Jayne any more, she was still stuck with her clothes. Today the outfit was bright pink cord dungarees and a fluffy white sweater beneath. She felt like a stick of rock—yet they certainly did something for her figure. Not that it mattered one jot what she looked like any more . . .

The living room felt chilly after the steamy shower and she could smell bacon and coffee and the radio was on. Heavens, she had forgotten it was Christmas!

Joshua looked dreadful. He came out of the kitchen carrying two loaded plates, his face was drawn, he hadn't shaved and there were dark smudges under his eyes. He was still wearing all the clothes he had worn yesterday. He looked rough and aggressive and there was a sort of earthy maleness about him that shouldn't have been sexually stimulating—but it was!

'I don't want all that,' she said sharply, because it was important that he shouldn't guess exactly how much she loved him.

'Today you eat.' He put the plates on the table and went back for the toast and coffee. Some day Kelly would be able to cook like that without shrivelling everything up and always burning the toast.

They ate in silence, or rather Joshua ate, and Kelly mostly chased the food around her plate.

'I thought you'd gone back to Washington,' she said, after a while. 'I mean last night—when you . . .'

'That's what you'd call wishful thinking,' he said grimly, and when she didn't answer he put his knife and fork down and pushed away his half full plate with a clatter. 'Did you really think I was letting you off that lightly?'

Kelly suddenly had difficulty in swallowing. The tension between them was almost tangible. She felt sick.

'Last night I didn't want to know, but now I do. Why—*Kelly*?' He said her name with contempt and she winced. 'Just tell me why. Why the whole goddamn lie right from the beginning?' He sounded very American, very big and tough and backwoodsy.

She shivered. 'I—because . . .'

'Because it seemed like a good idea at the time,' he finished for her.

Kelly's temper finally blew. 'Yes, that's just it. It did seem like a very good idea—and it *was* a very good idea; Jayne could never have coped with you.'

'And naturally you can,' he said cruelly.

Her bottom lip trembled. 'That's right.'

'Ha!' Then his hand shot across the table and he gripped her wrist painfully. 'Whose idea was it—Glenda's?' His dark eyes were brilliant slits in a savage face.

'No.' She was really angry now and she had had just

about as much as she could stand from Joshua Brett. 'No, it wasn't her idea—it was mine. *Mine*, do you hear?'

His gaze swept over her and she could tell he hated himself for doing it. 'That figures—one Osborn woman must be pretty much like any other.'

'You leave my family out of this!' Kelly wrenched herself free and sprang up from the chair, sending it sliding across the polished pine floor. 'And don't you become all sanctimonious with me, Joshua Brett. If you insist on behaving like some Victorian guardian, which, I might remind you, you're not,' she was backing away from the table, trying to get out of his reach, 'then you must expect people to retaliate. Did you really expect Jayne to drop everything and come over to eat humble pie in front of you?'

'Did she get the chance?' he interrupted, scraping back his own chair and striding towards her.

'What the hell do you mean by that?'

He looked suddenly pleased with himself. 'I mean, like maybe Jayne didn't get the chance to come. Maybe she could have used a break away from the hard London scene that you're always going on about.' He grabbed her wrist again and there was a brief struggle. His eyes glistened. 'Maybe little baby sister thought it was an opportunity too good to be missed? Did she?' He shook her. 'Did she, Kelly? Did she try and steal her sister's limelight because she was too hung up to organise a love-life of her own?'

Kelly kicked him hard—right on the shin. 'I wasn't very hung up last night, as I remember!' she practically shouted. 'You didn't seem to mind who I was then,' and through the turmoil some little part of her was crying out that this wasn't how it should have been. Hadn't she planned to tell him gently and he was supposed to have laughed and kissed her and said it didn't matter . . .

'*Mind* who you were!' Joshua repeated incredulously. 'What the hell sort of a game did you think you were playing? You'd gone about as far as you could go on someone else's reputation, honey. Didn't you realise I would have know as soon as ... only it would have been too late then.' He broke off and ran trembling fingers through his thick dark hair. 'Look, nineteen-year-old virgins aren't my scene—get it?' His voice and face were the cruellest things she had ever encountered, but still his eyes raked over her as if they had a devilish mind of their own. 'You still don't realise, do you?'

'Realise what?'

Joshua groaned. 'Don't look at me like that!'

'I'm not looking at you like anything.'

'If you think that, then it's about time someone showed you ... Look at you!' He was still holding one of her wrists and he turned her this way and that, as if he was selling her at a white slave market. 'You're like some sexy pink elf, all legs and big eyes.' His voice dropped to a husky growl. 'And it's about time you realised just what that innocent image does for a man!'

Rage burst from Kelly. Sexy pink elf! Who the hell did he think he was, anyway?

'And whose fault is it that I *didn't* find out?' she shouted back at him. 'Who was it that turned squeamish when they found out who I really was?' They glared at each other and the tension crackled between them. She was crazy, *crazy*, to be taunting him like this, but some devil made her do it. He was the most virile, exciting, sexually attractive man she had ever met, and in spite of everything she wanted him, here and now ... If he wouldn't take her in love, then maybe he would take her in anger. Anything was better than nothing at all ... and her mind went dizzy with the exhilarating danger of it all. Crazy—crazy ...

He grabbed both her shoulders and the soft white sweater was no protection from his cruel fingers.

'You don't know what you're saying—I'm not one of your fumbling adolescents!' He was shaking her; she stumbled, and as their legs tangled together he drew in a quick, sharp breath. 'I could have hurt you, Kelly. *Really* hurt you.'

'Ha!' She laughed in his face. 'I doubt it.'

He gasped, and the challenge danced in the air between them.

Kelly held her breath and Joshua fought to keep his under control. He wanted her; she knew that as well as she knew her own shattering desire. His whole body pulsated with aggressive male magnetism and the strong handsome face was strained in tortuous lines as the battle raged within him.

The challenge remained on Kelly's face as if it had a life of its own, as well, The tightly fitting dungarees accentuated shapely feminine curves. Only she didn't feel like a sexy pink elf, she felt like a wicked fairy who had boldly—recklessly—taken the initiative knowing perfectly well where it could lead her. Hadn't he just made that shatteringly clear?

From the radio in the kitchen came the sound of a choir singing carols, only that wasn't real. The only reality was the two of them, in this tiny cabin high in the Blue Ridge Mountains.

The grip on her shoulders increased so that she nearly cried out in pain. She could feel him burning up as a mixture of rage and sexual energy throbbed through him. Now. If he was going to make violent love to her it would be now . . .

Only suddenly it was over. He pushed her away and his voice was dry and ragged as he said, 'Didn't your mother ever tell you not to play with fire?' Then there was horror in his eyes as he realised the cruel tactlessness of his words.

But Kelly's mother had died so many years ago that she was beyond being hurt by unfortunate remarks. This time, however, Joshua's words brought the Osborn family crashing into her tiny world. Glenda. Jayne. And the real, hopeless reason that she had come to America. She was furious that this devil incarnate had made her forget. Furious—and frustrated.

'Maybe my mother didn't get the chance,' she bit back at him, 'but I'm surprised my father didn't warn me about you!'

'Kelly, I . . .'

She didn't want to hear what he had to say. 'But there was one thing he did tell us,' she interrupted quickly. 'He told us to look after each other. My girls, he used to call us. All *three* of us. And we still are— we're a family—his family,' her voice broke, but she recovered quickly. 'That's why I'm here, since you wanted to know so much.'

'And you're still trying to tell me that Glenda doesn't know?'

'No,' Kelly said awkwardly. 'At least, not to begin with.'

He pounced quickly. 'But she knows now?'

'Only since the other day—when I spoke to her on the phone . . .' What was the point of denying it?

'I don't believe you.' Joshua's face was dark with anger. 'You Osborn women are all the same—you don't give a damn. But did you really believe that by coming here you could *help* her position?'

'Foolish, wasn't it?' she snapped. 'But since meeting you I've realised how wrong we all were to imagine you might have a shred of humanity.'

'If you've discovered that, then your trip to America hasn't been entirely wasted,' he said coldly. 'Glenda's beauty farm really is that important?'

She turned away from him. Oh yes, it was important all right. And if he didn't lend her the money, bang went the London flat . . . Only she wasn't going to tell him that because somehow it didn't fit into the image of the Osborn women sticking together.

'Of course it's important—to us all,' she said, looking back at him over her shoulder. 'And I came because Jayne couldn't have coped with you—it's as simple as that.'

'Nothing's that simple.' Then his voice changed slightly. 'Jayne's been ill?'

'She's been under a very great strain,' Kelly corrected. 'She needed a quiet, relaxing holiday.'

'Why didn't you tell me when you phoned from London?'

'Would it have made any difference?'

He shrugged. 'Probably not.'

'Exactly!' Her voice was like ice.

'And so I take it that everything you've said, and done, has been nothing but a pack of lies, right from the moment you set foot in this country?'

She thought of yesterday and the ice storm; she thought of last night, and of all the other times of loving him—and she couldn't answer. The strained silence stretched into a dark abyss.

'Thank you for not trying to deny it,' he said eventually. 'But where exactly does that leave you?'

Her eyes widened at his sinister tone. 'What do you mean?' she whispered.

He closed the chasm between them, tangling his fingers into her damp hair. 'Where are *you*—beneath all the lies?' he said brutally. 'Maybe I want to find out the truth about you.'

'There's nothing to find out,' Kelly stammered as she tried to push him away. She didn't want him to be so cold and calculating—or did she?

He laughed bitterly. 'Of course there's something to find out. What sort of girl *dares* to try and fool me?' His eyes glistened dangerously. 'Maybe the real Kelly is even more interesting than big sister Jayne.'

'You don't know what you're saying . . .' But it was too late because he was kissing her, his lips hard and merciless, trapping hers, forcing her mouth to yield to him, and it was all hate and bitterness and ruthless possession . . . He forced their bodies together and the impact was heat and fire—and then, for some unaccountable reason, the heat softened their bones so that there was a moulding, and fusion. His lips gentled—and her arms coiled around his neck.

Kelly was lost in the timeless wonder of it all. Somehow the miracle had happened . . . And then she realised he was kissing Kelly, the real Kelly, for the first time. And there was a difference, a deep consuming difference . . . Suddenly she was responding with a wildness she hadn't known she possessed. Joshua groaned, equalled, then surpassed her passion.

Only instead of lifting her up and carrying her back to bed, he was pushing her from him, yet his hands remained firmly on her shoulders.

'Jos . . .' she began, but the sound died as she stared up at his face. His eyes were cold and hard, taking in her slim, youthful figure, her tousled hair and passionate eyes. Her petite, fresh femininity was a complete contrast to his rough, tough unkempt maleness. The dark shadows under his eyes matched the dark smudgy shadow of his unshaven chin. This was the man beneath the figure usually seen in Washington's slick social scene. Without the urbane polish he seemed even more powerful, and there was an earthy, almost neolithic sexuality about him that reached out and captured some primaeval instinct of her own.

'I'm going to get cleaned up,' he said gruffly, 'and while I'm doing so, you can pack.' He was halfway across the cabin before she found the strength to ask why. He stopped and turned round slowly, as if he was still thinking about something. His face was like ice. 'Because we're returning to Washington.' He had disappeared back into himself; the chasm was between them again, and this time Kelly couldn't see a way across.

'We can't,' she said frantically. 'I mean, it's Christmas.'

'I no longer feel like celebrating.'

'What about tomorrow—the bird count?' she tried again, and although they stared at each other she knew they weren't thinking about tomorrow—but were remembering yesterday instead.

'The bird count will have to do without us,' he said with a quiet calmness that terrified her. 'Another day out on that mountain with you, my dear Kelly, would be my idea of hell.'

He left her, and for a long time she remained absolutely still. She clung to the back of the settee and stared at the poor, dispirited fire. But she didn't see the fire, she saw only yesterday again; yet this time the ice storm, the bright shining crystal that had covered the trees, began to crack and splinter, and their shattered remnants felt like the hard broken pieces of her life that somehow had to be put back together again—without Joshua.

Trouble was—how?

CHAPTER TEN

KELLY'S vision had come true; the ice storm had gone, today the trees were grey again. She guessed the birds would be pleased: it was something.

They loaded the car in a grey silence; in fact everything was grey today. It had snowed in the night and the sky was still heavy with more to come. Kelly stood on the porch and shivered. It was so quiet, so still, until snow showered from the laden branch of a fir tree and fell to the ground with a plop. A little bird had hopped along the hand rail, leaving minute, criss-cross, pigeon-toed footprints. And suddenly she didn't want to leave this place that had given her a brief, yet total, glimpse of—what?—happiness? No, it had been more than that—but she couldn't think of another name for it. Whatever it was, it had been special between the two of them, and instinct told her that the mixture would never be the same again with anyone else.

Never the same again for Kelly—but did that necessarily apply to Joshua? Or course not. To him she had just been a possible affair. A brief encounter—a bit of fun. If his feelings had really been involved, he couldn't be doing this—he couldn't be packing up and clearing out of here without even trying to see her point of view. He thought her a scheming, cold-blooded female—and if he couldn't *sense* that all her kisses had been real, then how could mere words possibly persuade him?

And anyway, it wouldn't have worked, because marriage to Joshua wouldn't have been a life in a cabin in the Blue Ridge Mountains. It would have been jet-setting across the Atlantic, entertaining in Washington and London . . . and that didn't fit in with her plans, did it? She still had her degree to get—God willing. It was important to her; she didn't want a life shining in the rays of someone else's sun, even if that someone was

143

Joshua. She closed her eyes. Joshua . . .

He was still down at the car loading up, so she went back into the cabin for a last check round.

The fire was out, the cabin was dark and chilly, yet for a moment she imagined it alive and bright, the room warm and cosy again, and who would be sitting on the rug warming her toes and sipping Joshua's wine the next time he came?

They stopped at the Ranger's house on the way back, probably to tell him about the change of plans, she guessed. Joshua climbed out of the car and didn't invite her to follow. Not that she wanted to—the situation was embarrassing enough as it was. What excuse had he made? She didn't want to know. When he came back out, only a few moments later, there was still a goodbye smile on his face. But as soon as he saw the car, and Kelly sitting in it, the smile vanished and a cold rush of air chilled the warmth as he slid back into his seat.

'Is that where you went last night—for a drink?' she asked, and he just stared through the windscreen and nodded, as if he couldn't trust himself to speak.

He was angry, she could tell by the set of his shoulders and the aggressive way he gripped the steering wheel. The white road snaked ahead of them, twisting from one side of the mountain to the other. Joshua followed in the snow tracks of the one or two vehicles that had gone before him. Most people, Kelly realised, would be at home celebrating Christmas.

'The northern part of the Skyline Drive is closed,' said Joshua after a few miles. 'Apparently it's freezing up there.' He threw her the map. 'The next exit is Thornton Gap—which road do we take back to Washington from there?'

She sorted it out as he drove downwards through steep banks cutting through the mountain. Soon they were heading east on U.S. 211. The mountains were behind them now, it wouldn't take long to get back to Mclean—how long after that before he put her on a flight to Heathrow?

Home. London. Without Joshua . . . She averted her

face and stared out of the side window for most of the journey.

The roads had been cleared of snow and were free of traffic except for a few extra vehicles that appeared around lunchtime. Joshua kept the radio on, which fortunately made conversation impossible. They made good time and were back in Mclean soon after two. They had hardly got the front door opened when Rosey-from-next-door came bounding up the drive.

Kelly closed her eyes and groaned inwardly. Joshua would probably attract all females from the cradle to the grave.

'Hi there!'

She responded to the girl's cheerful greeting with a noncommittal grunt.

'And how's my Rosey-Posey today?' Joshua said affectionately, yet giving Kelly a thunderous look at the same time.

She didn't wait to hear any more, but picked up the box with the turkey in it and marched indoors.

Within five minutes the house seemed full of people. Rosey's mother arrived; she was smart and attractive, somewhere in her late thirties, and Kelly had been right, she was obviously as besotted with their English neighbour as her daughter. Yet the mother had a mature, friendly warmth that Kelly was instantly drawn to. Joshua responded differently too, his smile wasn't quite so bright and sparkling, it was more genuine—deeper. And his voice welcomed her in a way that made his earlier greeting to Rosey sound nothing more than casual friendliness.

'Pamela' was introduced. 'And you haven't met Kelly,' Joshua continued.

'*Kelly?* Oh, I thought . . .' Rosey's mother began.

Then it was Rosey's turn. 'But you said . . .'

Kelly never blushed—but this was something of an exception. Her face went tight with embarrassment and she couldn't think of anything to say.

'Jayne couldn't make it,' Joshua's firm, noncommittal

voice stopped further speculation, 'so Kelly came instead.'

Rosey was suspicious, but her mother looked as if she was used to getting things wrong.

'I've made you these candies,' she said, handing the gift-wrapped box to Joshua. 'We thought you were going to be away for Christmas...' There was a moment's confusion and then her husband arrived at the back door and the name Kelly or Jayne obviously meant nothing to him.

'I hope you're having a great Christmas, Kelly,' he boomed, shaking her hand with his giant paw, and somehow Joshua got them all out of the kitchen and into the drawing room. She heard him offering them drinks and a few moments later he came back into the kitchen to get a Coke for Rosey from the fridge.

Kelly turned on him, all her embarrassment stifled in rage.

'There was no need to deliberately make me look a fool!' she hissed, because all the doors were open and she didn't want the next-door crowd to hear.

Joshua wrenched the fridge door open. 'What did you expect? You're *Kelly*, remember? Everyone's going to have to get used to it.'

She suddenly thought of all the times she had dreamed of him calling her that. It hurt and she could have screamed.

'Look,' he slammed the door shut and all the bottles inside rattled, '*you* might be prepared to live a continuous lie, but I'm not. These people are my friends...'

'That's obvious,' she interrupted.

'... and I have no intention of deceiving them just to make things comfortable for you. So you can come and join us—or you can stay here. It doesn't matter either way to me.' He made for the door, but her quiet words pulled him up. 'Say that again,' he said sharply, turning back to face her.

'I *said*—I want to go home. Back to England. Now.'

'Sure.' He shrugged and her heart sank. 'There's the door,' he pointed. 'Start walking.'

'But...'

'No buts, Kelly. You're a big girl now, remember? You got yourself into this—*you* get yourself out.'

'You beast!' she flew at him, hair and face wild. 'You know I've got to get back to university . . .'

He fended her off with one hand. Luckily the can of Coke was still unopened.

'You should have thought of that.' He pushed her away. 'I'm just about sick and tired of you Osborn women—all of you—you've been nothing but trouble from the very beginning!'

He returned to his guests and Kelly marched around the room, fuming. So she had to get herself out, did she? Right. So she would phone Glenda. How much would a bus trip to Florida cost? Would they take her English credit card? She made herself a pot of tea and started planning.

The phone rang, or rather it trilled—and then there was that long American pause before it trilled again. Kelly stared at it. There were phones all over the house, it was up to Joshua to answer it. He didn't, and when it trilled for the third time she snatched it off the wall.

There was that long, squeaking, hollow sound of a long-distance call. Maybe it was Glenda. Good—just the person she wanted to speak to.

'Hullo,' she said again.

'Kelly?' the voice was faint, but unmistakable.

'Jayne!' Then Kelly remembered the people in the other room. 'Bit extravagant, isn't it?' she went on more quietly, 'phoning all the way from the Seychelles just to say Happy Christmas?'

There was a strange sound from the other end. 'I'm not . . .'

'Not in the Seychelles?' Kelly frowned.

'No—not phoning to say Happy Christmas,' said Jayne.

'What's happened?' Now she recognised the strange sound; Jayne was crying.

'Oh, Kelly, it's dreadful! It's done nothing but rain, and Derek's so—so aggressive—and it's been a simply frightful Christmas!'

Kelly couldn't think of anything to say. 'Er—what are you going to do?' she muttered helplessly.

'I want to come home,' Jayne sniffed miserably.

Don't we all? thought her sister. 'Well, why don't you?' she said instead.

'I don't mean *home*,' Jayne's voice wavered as it bounded between earth and satellite. 'I mean Washington. There's no reason for me to stay in London, and as you're there . . .'

Kelly managed to keep up with her disjointed reasoning.

'You can't—what about Joshua?'

'Does he still think . . .' Jayne began.

'No, no. He knows I'm me.'

'So it's all right, then.' Her sister sounded relieved. 'I felt a bit guilty about spoiling your scheme . . .'

'*My* scheme?' Really, some people had no appreciation!

'But if he knows,' Jayne went on, 'well, it might be nice to stay in America for a while . . . What's the matter, Kelly, why are you laughing?'

'Laughing? Me?' Kelly bit back the hysterical note in her voice. 'Why not, I mean—yes, come on over.' Joshua was sick and tired of all the Osborn women, was he? Good. Because now he was going to get them in double measure.

'I don't know about . . .' the connection momentarily exploded with static.

'What?' Kelly shouted.

'*Flights.* I don't know *when*—I'll just phone you when I arrive. It might take a few days.'

Their goodbyes were brief, and as Kelly put the receiver back the phone gave a satisfied ting.

She turned round to see Joshua standing in the doorway.

'Who was that?'

She told him.

'What did she want?'

She told him that, as well.

But instead of exploding, Joshua merely smiled maliciously. 'Well, well, well, how convenient!' And Kelly could almost believe that he had willed Jayne's new relationship to go wrong, and that by exerting some evil power he had caused the rains to fall unceasingly on the Seychelles.

A Christmas you will never forget, Joshua had threatened, and so it turned out to be. Apart from driving what felt like all over Virginia, loading and unloading the car more times than Kelly cared to remember, entertaining the next door crowd who finally left around four o'clock, there still remained the problem of the uncooked turkey.

They were back in the kitchen again, the table and floor still littered with their mountain of gear.

'I told you I can't cook. Why don't you go next door? You know they'd *love* to have you.'

'This is my house—and it's my Christmas dinner, and no one's driving me out—least of all you. If you can't cook I guess this is a good time to learn,' and he banged a cookery book on the table and stalked out.

'Don't you know how long it takes to cook a bird that size?' she shouted after him. 'We won't get to eat until midnight!' which was an exaggeration, but how would he know that?

The door opened again. 'You have a great deal of technical information for one who doesn't aspire to the culinary arts . . .'

Kelly hurled the book at him. 'Get out!' but he had already gone.

Boy, it was some Christmas, all right!

They were to dine by candlelight. It was Joshua's tradition and she was to take it as no kind of honour.

'You can go and get changed,' he said, coming into the kitchen. 'I'll see to the rest of it—go on.'

Reluctantly her eyes were all over him and she felt a momentary pang of despair. Tonight he was all immaculate sophistication. The shirt was silk and the dark blue jacket was a soft velvet that moulded itself across his shoulders and back with a cut so superb that

the eyes automatically travelled beyond, to the long lean
length of narrow hips, taut thighs ... The subtle scent
of his aftershave said everything about him; cool and
mysterious, yet with a certain musky undertone that
exactly matched the virile, male animal which she knew
lay beneath. But looking at him now, she saw not the
man on the mountain, but the man who had built Space
Design U.K. And he was here, in his Washington home,
surrounded by wealth and luxury—the trappings of hard
work and success ... She must have been mad to even
imagine that he could fall in love with her. Nineteen-
year-old virgins weren't his scene, he had told her, and
she could readily believe him.

'I'm going to make the brandy sauce—there's no need
for me to change.' Her voice was as brittle as her heart
felt.

'I *said*, I'll do it.' He pushed her aside. 'Go on—I'm
not sitting down with you looking as if you're dressed
to dig the garden—and I don't want my brandy sauce
lumpy, either.'

'This morning you said I looked like a sexy pink elf.'
Dig the garden? Cheek!

His face darkened. Lord, how handsome he was, even
now.

'I made a mistake.'

'You?' she tossed at him.

His eyes seemed to look inside himself, and he didn't
appear to like what he saw. 'Yes, even me—now *get*.'

Kelly took one more look at him, and 'got'.

A Christmas to remember! Huh!

The dining room was warm and mellow, the gold and
white image softened by candlelight and an open fire. A
piano concerto quietly filled the dark corners; it sounded
like Mozart, but no amount of carefully planned atmos-
phere could defuse the tension that crackled across the
table.

'I take it that's Jayne's dress,' said Joshua, when they
were halfway through the main course, which was sur-
prisingly edible. The little clock on the mantelpiece deli-

cately chimed nine-thirty, almost to itself.

Kelly nodded. 'Why do you ask?' She had chosen this red silk dress on purpose. It was quite extravagantly unsuitable for a quiet family dinner, but some devil had poured her into it. She knew Joshua had disapproved the moment he had set eyes on it. 'It's not too revealing, I hope,' she added wickedly. How did he know nineteen-year-old virgins weren't his style if he didn't know anything about them? It was about time he started thinking of her as a real woman . . . Fool, fool, warned a voice in the back of her mind.

He dabbed his lips with a crisp white napkin, then slowly picked up his glass of wine. 'Red doesn't suit you.' He twirled the crystal stem and looked down the table at her. 'And neither does bright pink.'

Kelly seethed and nearly threw her plate at him. So much for Mozart and candlelight! But the worst of it was, she knew he was perfectly right.

Kelly made the coffee. Ten-thirty. How much longer before she could escape from this ritual? It was dreadful being with him, loving him, hearing the sound of his voice, and knowing that he felt only contempt for her. She had to get away from here soon.

When she carried the tray through to the drawing room a glass of Cointreau was waiting for her on a little table by her chair. There was a gift-wrapped package as well, and she looked from it to Joshua as he stood with his back to the fire warming a glass of brandy between his hands.

'Merry Christmas.' His voice and eyes were dead. She hesitated and he shrugged. 'You might as well—it's no good to me. But there's no need to get excited.'

Excited! She wanted to hurl it at him—but even little virgins didn't act quite like that. She undid it, battling with the sticky tape. There was something soft inside . . . It was a thick woolly hat with a long matching Dr Who-type scarf. If they had still been in the mountains it was exactly what she would have needed tomorrow on the second day of the bird count.

Somehow she muttered thanks, but her voice choked

and she had to turn it into a cough. Her fingers sank into the springy softness. The wool was a shade somewhere between pale sherry and amber. It clashed dreadfully with the red dress, but it exactly matched her eyes.

Kelly escaped to bed with a sudden headache; Joshua made no attempt to stop her.

Christmas had been bad enough, but it turned out to be just a warming-up period for the weekend that was to come.

Kelly was forced to trail around to Sunday brunch, afternoon at-homes and elegant evening parties, to exclamations of delight as women everywhere saw Joshua.

'But we thought you were away . . .'

'Darling, I *knew* you couldn't desert us . . .'

'There's someone you simply must meet—I told her you weren't coming and she was so sad . . .' Joshua was whisked away on yet another cloud of chiffon and Chanel, and Kelly's continuous smile hardened as if it had been set in concrete.

She wasn't sure if socialising was worse, or whether being in the same house as Joshua, yet living totally separate lives, was even more so. During the day after Christmas, Saturday, and for the rest of the weekend, if they weren't out at a party, he spent hours working in the study. He was on the phone a lot, some were business calls, she could tell, but a lot more were hostesses who had just heard he was in Washington after all. Some invitations he accepted, and some he refused, but all in that brittle, lighthearted manner that she was coming to recognise as exactly matching the depth, or rather the shallowness, of his feelings. Work was the only thing that mattered to Joshua Brett—and work spelt Space Design U.K.

When the phone rang one particular time, Kelly was curled up on the sofa trying to catch up on the mountain of reading the university expected her to do during the holidays. She wasn't really listening to him, but she couldn't help hearing his firm, precise voice begin, 'My dear Jean . . .' and then she heard him walk across the study floor and close the door. It was fifteen minutes before the extension in the drawing room 'tinged' as he put down the receiver. Kelly read the same paragraph for the tenth time. The brunette at the Embassy—had her name been Jean?

That was it. She had had enough. Kelly flung down her book and marched across to the study.

'What is it?' Joshua replied to her firm knock, but he didn't look at her. He was staring into space, lost in his mind's wandering . . . Kelly checked herself. Of course not. The Brett mind would never wander.

'I want to have a word with you,' she began, and he blinked and suddenly saw her. It was quite obvious that he wished she had been someone else. 'I'd like to go home,' she said firmly. 'I know you said I've got to sort it out myself, but I've been thinking. It's the twenty-seventh today—my allowance is due at the end of the week. I can give you a post-dated cheque . . .'

'Absolutely not,' came the clipped response.

Wide, helpless eyes stared at him. 'Why?'

He stared back at her, still deep in his own thoughts. 'Because . . .' he stirred the air with an expressive hand, as if conjuring a reason, 'because your sister will be arriving shortly—and I have rather a busy week ahead of me.' He began moving papers on his desk as if the audience was over, but Kelly wasn't being put off so easily.

'Look—I have to be back by the ninth, anyway,' she said, stomping over and banging her fist on the mahogany desk top.

'There's no need to remind me.' He sifted through more papers and all she could do was gaze at the top of his dark head. 'We'll discuss it some other time.' And she sighed because the shutters were well and truly down and it would take an atomic bomb to rouse him—or a woman named Jean? 'By the way,' he added, as if confirming her thoughts, 'I shall be going out later—and I've no idea what time I shall be back. I'll make sure everything's locked up—and leave you next-door's phone number just in case.'

'I'm not a child!' Kelly retorted, but she couldn't stay to say more because it was obvious that in spite of everything that had happened between them, Joshua Brett would always regard Kelly as nothing more than a child. Jayne's kid sister. The epithet had stuck!

CHAPTER ELEVEN

JAYNE arrived in a snowstorm, or rather, it was snowing when she phoned Kelly from Dulles airport. It was five-thirty on Monday evening; Joshua hadn't arrived home yet.

'One of us will pick you up,' Kelly explained. With a bit of luck she could catch Joshua before he left the office. So she hung up quickly and phoned him. No reply. Not even a secretary, although perhaps they weren't back from the Christmas holiday yet.

After twenty minutes he still hadn't arrived and she realised that he could have gone anywhere and not be home for hours ... at six o'clock she put on her jacket and walked across to the garage. She was going to have to take out one of these monsters. They sat there looking sleek and smug—their cost in dollars measured by the yard. Kelly accepted the challenge and climbed into the station wagon; it looked a few feet shorter than the black limousine.

'What on earth happened to you?' said Jayne, when Kelly eventually found her in the Clipper Club. It was a quiet, green oasis tucked away from the mêlée of departure and arrival lounges. Jayne was sipping a gin and tonic and she offered one to Kelly.

'Better not—you haven't seen the tank I've got outside.' So they retrieved Jayne's baggage from the man behind the desk and staggered outside.

'Had a good flight?'

Jayne groaned. 'I managed to get a stop-over in London, so I picked up some of your clothes.' Kelly didn't say anything; she knew the pink dungarees and scarlet dress would look sensational on Jayne.

They piled the cases into the back of the car and Kelly went through the driving off procedure in the giant, unfamiliar automatic.

155

'What's been happening?' asked Jayne cosily, swivelling round in her seat, looking warm and sexy in a full-length fur coat and exquisite long boots.

'What's been happening?' Kelly repeated, and how easy it would have been to say, 'I've fallen in love, that's what's been happening, and I've ruined my life, because nothing will ever be the same again.' But instead she just shrugged and muttered, 'Nothing much.'

The windscreen was misty inside and as Kelly groped for a duster her gloved fingers pushed against a heavy metal key on the shelf. The key to the cabin. She remembered Joshua putting it there when they had left . . . Only she didn't want to think about the cabin. She found the duster and passed it to Jayne.

'Where's the de-mister?' her sister asked.

'Lord knows. Thanks, that's better,' and they drove on in silence. It wasn't their usual companionable silence, either. She could sense her sister's tension, guilt almost, as if none of this would have happened, and neither of them would be here, if Jayne had had more success handling men.

That was a laugh! How could anyone be expected to handle men if Joshua Brett was an example of the species? She should be saying something to put Jayne at her ease, but it would have to wait; right now this tank of a car needed her complete concentration.

When they reached Mclean and finally nosed into the driveway, Kelly let out a sigh of relief. It was snowing quite heavily again, and beginning to freeze.

The lights were on in the garage; Joshua's sporty four-seater was back.

'Not bad,' muttered Jayne, eyeing first his row of cars and then the elegant house, porch lights welcoming, the Christmas wreath a vivid splash of green and red against the white front door.

Kelly began unloading the suitcases and Jayne came back to help. The two girls were still burrowing in the back of the car when they both sensed a movement behind them.

It was Joshua. His footsteps had been silent in the snow.

'I tried to phone you,' Kelly wanted to say, but somehow the words died on her frozen breath. Joshua was staring at her as if she had been resurrected from the dead. So that was what he thought of women drivers! 'This is Jayne,' she said instead.

At last he realised that she wasn't alone. 'Welcome to Mclean,' he said automatically, but there was none of the contempt and hostility in his voice as when he had first met Kelly. His eyes flicked back to the younger sister's face. 'I've only just got home—I didn't know where you'd gone. What were the roads out there like?'

'It's all right, I haven't damaged the car—and I take it my driving licence is valid here for a month.'

He nodded, then he was taking the cases and hustling them inside. Kelly noticed he was still wearing his smart velvet-collared coat, and the lights were on all over the house. It looked as if he had run through it, searching for something in a very great hurry.

They all trooped upstairs, even the lights in her own room were on—funny! Jayne was chatting away happily about her flight. Kelly wasn't listening because this was the first chance she had had to get a really good look at her sister. And what she saw made her want to smile. With her coat and matching fur hat, Jayne looked like someone out of *Anna Karenina*; all femininity wrapped in sable, or whatever it was. How could she have hoped to impersonate her sister? In looks and experience they were worlds apart. And it was obvious that Joshua thought so too. Kelly recognised that look in his eyes; she had seen it all too many times before. Only Jayne wasn't someone they would only meet at parties; she would be here in the house, living with them . . . Kelly wasn't sure if she could stand the full blast of the Brett charm twenty-four hours a day!

'Rather nice,' said Jayne, when he had left them to unpack.

'Don't even try,' warned Kelly. 'He eats little girls like us for breakfast.'

'Like *us*?' Jayne queried.

Kelly pretended not to notice her insinuation. 'Tell me about the Seychelles,' she said, flopping down on the bed, and Jayne groaned and began her horror story, and with a safer topic Kelly gradually relaxed.

It seemed that nothing much had happened to her sister, just another love affair that hadn't worked out. The continuous rain hadn't helped, Jayne said, but shouldn't such inclement weather be a boon to lovers? Kelly imagined being in the cabin, snowed-in with Joshua ... No, she didn't want to think about the cabin.

The suitcases were empty and there was a large mound of her own clothes on Jayne's bed. Kelly scooped up an armful.

'I'll just get your things,' she said, so they swopped clothes, or rather, the clothes were returned to their rightful owners. Even the nighties and flimsy broderie anglaise negligee went back and a pair of striped pyjamas and thick, plaid dressing-gown took their place. Kelly hurled them across her bed. Ugly, sexless things, she would never wear them again. Which meant she would go to bed naked from now on, even though there was going to be no one about to notice.

Jayne settled in as if she had always lived in Mclean. Joshua went to work Tuesday and Wednesday mornings before the girls were up and he spent both evenings working in his study. Kelly had the impression that he had a big business meeting coming up. Thursday was New Year's Eve and Kelly had woken to hear him leaving early again. It wasn't yet seven-thirty, it was still dark—and she thought how she would have hated it if they had been sleeping together and he had left her so soon. She snuggled down. But perhaps they would have set the alarm for six—that would have given them an hour to wake up slowly together—to make love ... She squeezed her eyes tight shut so that the tears couldn't escape. Stop it—you're only torturing yourself. She got up quickly and started being busy.

'Has he—said anything?' she asked Jayne, when they were halfway through breakfast.

'About . . .?'

Kelly nodded.

Jayne shook her head and nibbled her muffin. 'Not a word. Maybe he sympathises, after all.'

'Huh!' Kelly took her plate over to the dishwasher. 'It'll come—it's just that he's switched off family matters at the moment—there's something big coming up . . .'

'I think you're wrong,' said Jayne carefully. 'I don't think he will say anything. I'm sure you've misjudged him.'

Kelly came back to the table and perched on a stool. 'Maybe you're right at that,' she muttered numbly. And perhaps Jayne was right, perhaps he had been aggressive towards Kelly because instinctively he hadn't liked her. Maybe he would really help Jayne after all. For their father's sake, if nothing else.

'And would he be taking us out to these New Year parties tonight if he wasn't somewhere near human?' Jayne went on. 'He's had invitations to three, and he says we'll go to all of them.'

'Not me.' Kelly began clearing away the table, already she knew where everything went. 'It's your turn—you go with him. After all,' she added, trying to laugh, 'you're the one with the evening dresses now. And red doesn't really suit me.'

'There's the blue one.'

Kelly shook her head. 'I've already worn it.'

'Then buy a new one. Let's have a shopping spree.'

'No. Jayne, I don't want to go—really.' Her sister tried not to look too pleased.

The morning stretched ahead of them. They had done the White House and the Air and Space museum yesterday. Kelly suggested more sightseeing, but Jayne wrinkled her nose.

'Let's have a shopping spree, anyway,' she said, her eyes brightening at the thought of yet more clothes.

'Can you afford it?' It would never have occurred to Kelly to ask before now.

'There's always plastic money,' Jayne reminded her, and when Kelly looked disapproving, she said, 'Our allowances will be through today, it's the end of the year, Kelly. That's what credit cards are for. I'll be in funds again long before the bills come through.'

So they drove into D.C. and Kelly trailed around the stores, but it was only when Jayne bought her third item, frilly silk blouse this time, and handed over her credit card, that Kelly suddenly had her idea. If it applied to Jayne, then it would apply to Kelly as well. After the New Year break the cheque would come through to Kelly's bank in London. So she could buy a plane ticket home on her credit card and she wouldn't have to pay for it until February . . . Simple. She wouldn't have to go begging to Joshua . . . She was just about to tell Jayne when something cautioned her to stop. Best not tell anyone, because if Joshua found out he would find some other way of spoiling her plans—although goodness knows why.

Jayne was in high spirits as they drove back to Mclean. It was four o'clock and the threatened snow made the clouds full, dark and heavy. Kelly kept her eyes open for the sort of place where she could buy her air ticket. Maybe she could make an excuse and pop out later on.

The phone was ringing as, with arms full of Jayne's parcels, they battled their way between screen door and back door.

Kelly dumped everything down on the kitchen table and snatched up the receiver. Perhaps it was Joshua . . .

'Kelly?'

Her momentary excitement died. It was Glenda.

'Kelly, is that you? What the hell's going on up there?'

'How d'you mean?' Yet she knew what was coming almost before Glenda said it.

'I've just heard from my lawyers.' If it was warm down in Florida, none of the warmth had found its way into her stepmother's voice. 'They tell me the deal is off—Joshua has refused to lend me the money.'

'Oh! I'm sorry.'

'Sorry! Too right you should be sorry, honey. He

knows, doesn't he? When did he find out?'

'Er . . .'

Jayne had brought the rest of the things in. 'Who is it?' she mimed, unbuttoning her Anna Karenina outfit.

'Look, Glenda,' Kelly tried, and Jayne's eyes widened in sympathy. 'He just knew, himself, over Christmas . . .'

'And I bet he wasn't exactly over the moon about it.' Kelly pulled a face. 'You could say.'

'You realise it's all your fault? If you'd let Jayne come over, like I said, none of this would have happened.'

'She's—er . . .'

'No, no,' whispered Jayne, but it was too late.

'. . . here now,' Kelly finished. 'Yes—Jayne. What? Oh, since Monday. She wants to speak to you,' said Kelly, holding out the receiver, and her sister smothered a groan.

Jayne didn't say much beyond, 'Yes, Glenda. No, Glenda,' and as she stood with the phone held away from her ear, Kelly could easily hear what was being said.

'You realise, both of you, that now I shall be forced to sell the London flat?'

'Yes, Glenda.'

'It's about time you girls learned to stand on your own two feet.'

Kelly put the kettle on and it helped to drown the noise. She found the teapot and china mugs and the tea was brewing just as Jayne was managing to say goodbye.

'It's really all my fault,' she said, putting the phone down and turning towards Kelly. 'I know you did it for the best, but I should have come and faced him myself. Then none of this would have happened.'

'Don't kid yourself. If Joshua doesn't want to lend her the money, it's because she obviously isn't a good business risk. *We* won't have anything to do with it. He wouldn't let *emotion* come into it. He doesn't have any. Do you know, he once told me he wouldn't rekindle an old affair on principle. On *principle*! I ask you. How much more cold-blooded than that can you get?'

'I still think it's rotten of her to sell the flat,' Jane persisted. 'Can she? I mean, didn't Daddy's will say that she always had to provide us with a home?'

'There'll be a home for us in Florida, technically, I suppose. After all, she is American. I'm sure Daddy's executors will sympathise. *I'm* all right—there's university to go back to and I have friends to stay with during the holidays . . .' The tea was ready now, so she poured them both a mug. 'But what about you? How will you manage?'

Jayne shrugged. 'Stay on here for a bit, I suppose, and see what turns up.'

They were still in the kitchen, Jayne perching on the table, and Kelly propping up the sink, when they heard a car pull into the drive.

'He's early,' said Kelly, glancing at the wall clock.

'So would you be with a heavy night in front of you,' grinned her sister.

Kelly's heart dropped. Jayne's instinct for survival was incredible. A few minutes ago she had had a secure home in London pulled out from under her feet, and immediately she was looking round for something, or someone, to take its place.

The back door swung open sharply and Joshua came in with the cold. Suddenly the room was alive with the feel of him. His tall, powerful body was sending out masculine pulses of its own.

Both women in the room responded in their own way. Kelly, silent as the force of love she felt for him suddenly hit her, and Jayne, who smiled, looking genuinely pleased to see him. And after a cursory nod to Kelly, it was to Jayne he returned one of his own devastating smiles.

'Would—you like some tea?' Kelly managed to mutter.

'No, thank you,' he replied formally. 'I'm going into my study—and I'd like a word with Jayne.'

'What did he say?' asked Kelly, sitting crosslegged on her sister's bed as Jayne got ready for the party.

She smiled secretly. 'Not a lot. He asked me what plans I had for working in the New Year.' She picked up each of her three evening dresses in turn and held them in front of her. 'Which one do you think?'

'They're all fine. So what did he say?'

'Well, we chatted for a bit,' and there was a sideways glance at Kelly as she said this. 'And eventually I realised that he was sort of suggesting that I might like to stay over here—permanently.'

'Oh!'

'I really do think the red one suits me best, don't you?'

There was a knock at the door. 'Jayne—ten minutes.'

'Fine!'

'Where's Kelly?'

'She's in here.'

'I'll wait downstairs.' They heard him move along the landing.

'Doesn't he know you're not going?'

Kelly shook her head. 'He won't worry, though,' and she was right.

As both girls came down the stairs, Joshua only had eyes for Jayne and the stunning red dress. Although really there was more Jayne than dress, and his eyes gleamed with unholy satisfaction. Then he noticed Kelly for the first time and a dark eyebrow was raised in silent question.

'I'm not coming,' she said with her chin up.

'So I gather,' yet his eyes lingered over her tight old jeans and floppy white sweater with its appliqué lazy-daisies. It felt comfortable to be in her own clothes again, but it was pretty obvious which sister's wardrobe he preferred.

He helped Jayne into her coat, his hands resting on her shoulders a little longer than was necessary. They made a good pair; Jayne petite yet seductive, Joshua tall and aggressively male. Tonight he looked devastating in formal dinner jacket and bow tie. The white silk shirt had minute tucks down the front—and his black shoes were hand-sewn and positively gleamed. As he shrugged himself into his coat and picked up car keys and gloves, Kelly caught a faint hint of his aftershave and she remembered how much sharper it had seemed when she had kissed his neck.

'Happy New Year in advance,' said Jayne, with a sudden pang of guilt. She gave her sister a hug. 'It won't be half so much fun without you.'

When Jayne lied, she did it with style. Kelly managed to grin. 'Go on!' she gave her sister a little push. 'Have a super time.'

'Goodnight,' was all that Joshua said, and his face and eyes were remote.

'Night,' mumbled Kelly, looking down at her chin. She just about got the door shut before the first tear came.

There was a tap on her bedroom door and Kelly was instantly awake. She rolled over and peered at the luminous dial of her watch. It was almost four-thirty. Surely Jayne wasn't going to give her a blow-by-blow account of the party now?

The tap came again.

Kelly rolled back and called, 'Come in,' only it wasn't Jayne holding up her evening dress who came tiptoeing in when the door opened. Instead it was Joshua's dark figure silhouetted against the light.

'What d'you want?' she mumbled, throat suddenly tight, as she struggled with the bedside light. She found the switch at last, but it only made a soft pool of light over her bed, the rest of the room was all dark, menacing shadows. Her heart began banging as it recognised her tension. 'Is anything the matter?' she tried again. Perhaps there had been an accident.

'Everything's fine.' He came into the well of soft light, tall and proud, staring down at her. His shirt was open at the neck, his bow-tie undone and hanging loose, and although he was wearing his dinner jacket, Kelly had the distinct impression that he had just slipped it back on. Where had he come from? The rest of the house was silent.

'Where's Jayne?'

He smiled briefly. 'Asleep. She had quite a night.'

Kelly began to sit up, until she caught sight of her pyjamas and dressing gown over the back of a chair. What had possessed her to begin sleeping naked? She clutched the covers tightly, but her shoulders were still bare and her dark hair brushed lightly against smooth, fair skin.

'I could have waited until morning to hear all about it,' she said tightly.

'I shan't be here in the morning—that's why I've come now.' And to her amazement he smoothed himself a patch of bedclothes and sat down.

Kelly moved her legs quickly, wishing it was a narrow single bed instead of this voluptuous king-size.

'I'm going into the office early,' Joshua said quietly, 'and from there I'm going on to London.'

She stared at him, large amber eyes in a sleepy, woe-begone face. He looked away quickly.

'Jayne's going down to Florida,' he went on, and Kelly's eyes widened even more.

'I don't think she ought to. You see, we spoke to Glenda earlier today,' she said hurriedly, 'and she wasn't very happy with us.'

'Can you blame her?' He leapt to Glenda's defence so naturally that Kelly thought, he does still love her in spite of everything. 'But we've spoken to her again this evening—and I've arranged it all. I want Jayne and Glenda to get a few things sorted out—and it seems an ideal time for her to go—while I'm away.'

'*I'm* not going.' Kelly's mind was working overtime. It was all turning out better than she could have hoped. With Joshua away and Jayne down in Orlando, it would be easy to buy her ticket and fly home. 'I'm not exactly Glenda's favourite person, right now,' she went on breathlessly, and then because it was worth a try, she added, 'I suppose you wouldn't take me back to London with you?'

'No.'

'But the new term starts . . .'

His eyes were dark and watchful. 'You're determined to get this degree?'

'Absolutely.'

He nodded, as if he expected that answer. 'I'll be back on the seventh—we'll talk about it then.'

Kelly glared at him. 'You're impossible!'

'Very likely.' He sat further back on the bed and Kelly flinched. Why didn't he get out of here? She could sense dark, mysterious thoughts behind that handsome, stern face. 'But if you want to stay in Washington while I'm away, that's fine by me. I'll let them know next door . . .'

'Can't you understand that I'm not a child?' she blazed at him. 'I'm perfectly capable of living on my own without a baby-sitter on call. And anyway, it'll be good practice, won't it?'

'Practice for what?' His eyes were all over her, taking in her tousled hair, her face, her slim naked shoulders and the bright, angry light in her eyes.

Kelly clutched the bedclothes higher. 'If Jayne stays over here I'm going to be completely on my own in London, aren't I? Which you are perfectly well aware of too. So don't pretend to be concerned now, because I know you're not concerned about anyone except yourself.'

'We'll talk about it when I get back.' He was really angry now. Good. It wouldn't do him any harm to hear a few more home truths.

'Typical!' she threw at him. 'Business first. Never mind that I might have a few problems that need sorting out. Your trip to London is all you care about. You won't even *think* of me again until you walk back in that front door!'

'And how else do you account for all this?' he retorted, waving a hand around the room, but Kelly knew he meant everything; the whole house in Mclean, his successful international business, his home in Gloucestershire . . . 'Do you think all this comes from having my head full of cottonwool fantasies?'

'I'm not a fantasy—look,' she said, holding out her

arm and making him notice she was flesh and blood.

He took both her shoulders and shook her. He was close, very close, and she was eyeball to eyeball with the tangled dark hairs visible between the open front of his shirt. The faint smell of him overpowered her with its erotic mixture of spice and warm maleness. Her senses swam with the bittersweet intoxication of her sudden need for him. Would it never end—never?

'No, you're not a fantasy. I haven't made up my mind *what* you are. But do you think it would do any good if I worried about it *now*? I have a week of important conferences—that's what needs my attention. You'll be here when I get back—it will be time for you then.'

'There'll never be a time,' because I won't be here when you get back, she added silently to herself, but she wasn't going to tell him that. 'Let me go!' She pushed against him and he broke free. 'You're never going to get anywhere with a woman until you learn to put her first.'

Joshua stood up again, tall and remote. 'Don't be childish,' he said, turning away, and that was it—he had said it once too often. Kelly hurled the pillow at him with all her strength—two-handed.

He spun back again, anger brittle on his face, until he saw the bedclothes crumpled around her waist, and instantly the anger changed to wicked pleasure.

Kelly gasped and covered herself, but it was too late. He had seen her and now he wanted her—she knew him well enough to recognise his immediate desire.

'Be here when I get back.' The rich deep voice smouldered in the room's shadows.

Kelly caught her breath again. Could he read her mind? Did he know she was planning to escape?

'I don't have much option, do I?' she muttered, but he took a step nearer and with one finger, lifted up her chin.

'Be here,' he repeated, 'because if you aren't I shan't rest until I find you!'

Kelly had her eyes tight shut, but she opened them as he gave a muffled groan, and suddenly she wasn't in bed any more, but was being pulled out of it and Joshua was kissing her, his hands deliciously exciting as they moved to all the right places.

She clung to him, half in need—and half in modesty. Her feet weren't touching the floor, and she wanted desperately to coil her legs around his and draw herself even closer. But she fought with herself and she fought with him. How dared he come straight from her sister's bed to her own?

'Let me go—I hate you!'

He laughed, his eyes half closed slits searing over her. 'If it wasn't so late I'd prove you wrong, little lady.'

'Just get out of here!' She struggled in his arms and he tumbled her on to the bed. Then his laughter vanished. 'My God, you're beautiful!' His voice was husky with the strain of physical arousal. 'If only you were Jayne . . .'

'Jay . . .' But her outrage was cut off as a firm hand clamped over her mouth.

'If you were Jayne I would take you now—quickly.' His breath was ragged as he fought for control. 'But I'm not in the mood for a long, slow session. Look at the time, I have to be up in a couple of hours.' As he spoke he caressed her in just the right spot to drive her senseless. 'We need a whole long night together, my little Kelly. It would be a pity to break such a fragile flower simply through impatience.'

The spasm of pleasure passed and Kelly caught her breath again. 'I thought I wasn't your style,' she managed to gasp. 'And if you want Jayne she's next door—go on!' She gave him a shove, and to her utter dismay he sat up and looked around for his bow-tie that had fallen off in the struggle.

'I *do* hate you, Joshua Brett.' Amber eyes glistened with unshed tears. 'Just you remember that while you're in England.'

He looked weary now, as if the battle with himself had been even more fierce than the one on the bed.

'You have a lot to learn about the ways of men and women. I know you're far too young for me—but,' he looked past her, 'maybe it would be rather nice to teach you.'

'I wouldn't count on it,' she mumbled, trying to cover herself again.

He was walking away. How *could* he, if he really felt anything for her? Then he paused by the door and came back again.

'I think you'd better give me your passport.'

'What!' Ice rushed through her veins.

'You heard.'

'You've got no right—it's my property!'

Joshua picked up her bag and threw it on to the bed.

'It isn't in there,' she said, 'and anyway, what use is it to me, you know I don't have the fare . . .'

'Maybe not. But I don't trust you—as much as *that*,' he added, snapping his fingers. 'Where is it, Kelly? I'll ransack this room, believe me.'

She did. 'It's in there,' she muttered, nodding towards the bedside drawer. 'What are you going to do with it?'

'I'll put it in my safe—so don't even *think* you can get it, unless you want the local police department arriving on the scene.' He took the passport out of its wallet and noticed her few loose ten-dollar bills in the drawer beside it. So he took some money out of his own wallet and put it with hers.

'There's plenty of food in the house, and William will be back at the end of next week, but this is just in case you need anything.'

'I don't want your rotten money! You can't buy *me*, Joshua Brett.'

'I'm counting on it,' he said sharply. 'Now lie down and get some sleep.'

'I was asleep. *You* woke me up.'

He switched off the bedside light—the room was in sudden blackness.

'Goodnight, Kelly.' His voice broke her heart.

'I'm not speaking to you—ever again. Why don't you get out of my life and leave me in peace?'

CHAPTER TWELVE

'YOU'LL be all right? You're sure?'

Kelly gave her sister a gentle shove. 'Go on, you'll miss your plane. Of course I'll be all right. If I come I'll only foul things up between you and Glenda.'

Jayne heaved her case towards the baggage check-in. 'I didn't mean about this trip—I meant if I do stay on in America. Joshua's . . .'

'Yes?'

Both sisters stood still again and people flowed around them like a swift eddy around rocks.

'He's got some plan,' Jayne began, and for a moment Kelly wondered if it was anything to do with the beauty farm. Then she remembered that Joshua wasn't part of that deal any more, so he would be hardly likely to interest himself in the matter of Glenda's staff.

'Did he say what his plans were?'

Jayne shook her head. 'Glenda knows—he told her something on the phone last night . . .' She broke off awkwardly, and Kelly guessed that more than a phone call to Florida had happened last night. What promises had Joshua made? Was Jayne about to embark on another disastrous affair?

'Look, you don't have to explain to me,' she said quickly. This was the last thing Kelly wanted to hear. Couldn't Joshua organise his love-life less publicly?

Jayne gave her sister a goodbye hug. 'And you do have your degree, don't you?' she said. She was looking for excuses, as if she was about to take something away from Kelly and knew it was going to hurt her.

Kelly bit back the pain. 'Jayne Osborn, will you get on that plane and stop fussing! Have you any idea how much reading I should have done this holiday? I can't wait for a quiet week without any interruptions!'

At last Jayne left for Florida and Kelly returned to

Mclean. She was getting used to the big, heavy station-wagon now, but the road signs were still unfamiliar and the traffic lights, swinging from wires suspended across the roads, still took a bit of getting used to. Today they swung quite violently in the wind, and she wondered what would happen in a gale.

The house was strange and silent. Good, that was what she wanted, wasn't it? She threw off her jacket and scarf and raced up the shallow, curved staircase. She found the pile of thick paperbacks in her room and wandered downstairs again. Suddenly there were so many rooms to choose from and she didn't know where to go.

Everywhere was white and gold elegance; the drawing room looked like a film set . . . and there weren't any comfortable chairs in the dining room or kitchen. In the end she settled for the textured comfort of Joshua's study. It would be dark soon, so she switched on the table lamps, drew the heavy curtains, lit the fire and pulled the settee up in front of it.

At last settled comfortably, she opened her book at chapter seven. It was headed, *Sociological Machiavellianism and Ethics*. Kelly blinked, and her eyes drifted towards the fire . . . She shouldn't be sitting here reading, she ought to be thinking of a way to get back her passport.

Where was the safe? In here? She threw down the book and searched round, peering behind pictures, running her hand along the bookshelves in case there was a hidden spring. It was useless, and even if she found it, what good would it do? She wasn't studying for a degree in crime, and she didn't know any safe-breakers either.

She went back to the book and forced herself to read half a page, then the phone rang.

'No, he's away,' she sighed. 'About a week.' Joshua's women had started checking up on him already.

Kelly slept restlessly in the empty house that night. Jayne phoned Sunday morning to announce her safe arrival in Orlando and then there was nothing left to do except wade through the mountain of pages that constituted the Sunday papers.

It snowed in the afternoon and she had answered six more phone calls by teatime.

No, he hadn't left a phone number to reach him by, she said in exasperation. And to another question, 'No, I'm *not* the maid!'

That did it! Why the hell should she stay here and be his unpaid answering service? There wasn't the slightest chance of getting any real work done. Instead of drifting about the place she ought to be thinking of a way to get out of here. But where could she go? And what point was there—because hadn't Joshua threatened to find her?

She tried to watch a T.V. movie that evening, but the phone kept ringing and in the end she left it off the hook. She couldn't stay here—it was absolutely impossible; in every room there were reminders of Joshua—his anger, his contempt, and his unveiled desire.

Suddenly she thought of the cabin, where everything had been so different for a tiny, tiny moment of their time. She could spend a whole week up there, Joshua wouldn't be back in the States until next weekend. Maybe without phone interruptions she could get some work done. There was plenty of food in the cabin—but how would she get in?

Then she remembered that the key had been in the car when she had collected Jayne from the airport last Monday. Was it still there? Fingers crossed, she raced out to the garage . . . Whew! It was still there. She came indoors again slowly, thoughtfully, in spite of the snow flurries and bitter wind. She was tossing the heavy key up and down in her hands. Why not? Maybe for a few days she could relive her brief happiness. Maybe it would be some sort of comfort—a way of being close to Joshua again. She knew she would never feel close to him in this house; this house spelt Washington and all the brittle social life it entailed.

Pity it was dark. Kelly resolved to set the alarm and make a very early start on Monday morning.

*   *   *

She was almost within sight of the Blue Ridge Mountains when the idea struck her. Didn't people often lose their passports? Couldn't she apply to the Embassy for a replacement? If it hadn't been a dual carriageway she would have executed a swift U-turn . . . but as she slowed down and looked for a suitable place to change direction, she suddenly thought of all the questions they were bound to ask. Who was she staying with in Washington? Who was her next of kin? And how could she explain all that to Glenda? Then they would want to contact Joshua . . . She increased speed again and forgot the idea. Nice thought, but a bit impractical.

The journey took longer than the first time. Kelly reached the mountains fairly easily, but it was a question of picking her way after that; all mountain tracks looked very much like one another. It was nearly lunchtime when she pulled into the little layby at the foot of the steps. There was still a lot of deep snow lying about, unlike Washington which had only had a couple of inches.

It was like coming home. The key was a bit stiff, but at last she was inside. It was cold, and Joshua wasn't here—but everything else said 'hullo' to her. She had been right to come.

The electricity worked. The fire was awkward, but eventually ignited itself when her back was turned. Typical! A real Joshua Brett fire.

No, she mustn't think of him. She had five days here in peace and solitude, during which time she had to come to terms with the fact that he would never be hers, never love her . . . and what was somehow worse, never have the joy of loving anyone himself. Unless, in his strange way, he still loved Glenda . . .

It snowed heavily in the night, and the next morning she uncurled herself from the sleeping bag in front of the fire, and was determined to enjoy herself, in spite of everything.

She cleared the steps and put salt on them. Then she fed the birds, found a shed half full of logs, which was a relief. And after staggering to the back porch with enough to last her for a couple of days, she went back indoors, fixed breakfast, then settled down to her first real day of study.

Jayne had been right; this degree was important to her. Not because she particularly wanted a dazzling career, but because, with luck and plenty of hard work, it might open doors where she could actually be of some use in the world.

Wednesday felt different from the very first moment she opened her eyes. Through her sleepy haze Joshua seemed very close, and Kelly snuggled down for a bit longer. How easy it was to drift back in time and imagine how it had been—lying here with him . . .

She closed her eyes and could feel a quickening inside as if Joshua was really here again, his body hard and smooth, his hands warm, coaxing, magical. And then she remembered Washington again, the night before he left for England . . . *'If you were Jayne I would take you quickly . . .'* and in her solitude she cried out with the pain of wanting him now—quickly—anyway . . .

Her peace of mind had gone for the rest of the day. She tried to read, but afterwards could hardly remember a word of it. She went for a walk, or rather, a flounder in the snow. The car in the layby was well covered and the track up to the road looked almost impassable. For the first time it occurred to Kelly that maybe she wouldn't be able to get back to Washington by the weekend. Still, if she was snowed in, it meant that Joshua was snowed out, so all his threats about coming to find her would be pointless.

She had supper early that evening, cleared away the dishes, made up a really good fire and settled down to mend a cushion cover that was bursting open. She was beginning to feel comfortable again. The feeling that Joshua was close was absolute nonsense. He was in London, probably having a business lunch right now. He still had two more days of meetings—and he wouldn't have thought about her once.

There was a concert on the radio, something of

Prokofiev's—loud, exciting, discordant. Kelly put down
her sewing for a moment . . . No, of course it wasn't a
car outside; there was just the wind and snow. Instinctive
fear had turned to excitement—and then died again. She
picked up her needle and thread. There *was* someone
out there—banging snow off their boots on the front
porch. She held her breath. Of course it wasn't Joshua.
Who, then? Perhaps she ought to be very quiet and pretend there was no one here.

The handle turned and someone tried the door, but it
was securely locked, so was the back door . . . but
someone could break in through the windows.

The door rattled again and Kelly threw down her
sewing and quietly picked up the poker. She stood in
the middle of the room, heart hammering, feet apart,
face set with determination.

'Kelly, open the door! I know you're in there!'

Silence as her mouth dropped open in absolute aston-
ishment. There was only the sound of the wind and the
crackling fire.

'Kelly, I mean it—I'll break down this door!'

'No!' It rattled furiously. 'Wait—I'm coming!' and she
had only just pulled back the bolts when the door burst
open and Joshua stomped in, bringing the wind and
snow with him.

He slammed the door behind him and Kelly backed
away. The shock of seeing him was swiftly followed by
an even greater shock at the way he looked. He brushed
snow off his jacket and almost shook himself like some
proud, wild animal coming in out of the storm. But it
was his face that really astounded her. The usually aris-
tocratic features were strained, tired, almost haggard, as
if he hadn't slept more than an hour since they had last
met. She wondered if he was ill—then realised that he
would hardly be here if that were the case.

'What—are you doing here?' she stammered, as he
shrugged himself out of the jacket. He was wearing his
black cord jeans and polo sweater which moulded his
magnificent male shape, making him look more dangerous and predatory than ever.

'I've come to take you back to Mclean,' he said angrily. 'Just what the hell are you doing up here?' His eyes flashed round the room, searching for danger.

'I'm alone,' she snapped.

'So I see.'

'Who do you think I'd have with me? I don't know anyone.'

'I've been gone five days.' He moved nearer the fire, the room seeming filled with the relentless energy he brought with him.

'And you think I'm capable of picking up someone and bringing them here?' He looked as if he wished he hadn't opened his mouth, but Kelly was in no mood to forgive. 'You're despicable!' she choked. 'But why bother anyway? I'd be out of the way, out of *your* way— why don't you go down to Florida, I know Glenda and Jayne will be delighted to see you.'

He strode back round the settee, finally wrested the poker from her hand, and pulled her over to the window.

'Look at it out there,' he grated. 'What damn fool idea was it to come up here alone at this time of year? You saw what the roads were like at Christmas. I only just got through tonight.'

'How did you know I was here?' she asked primly, yet trying to wrench herself free at the same time.

'Intuition. And the knowledge that maybe you were just crazy enough.'

She was still struggling and he still wasn't letting her go.

'It's not my fault that you've dragged all the way up here. I don't even know what you're doing in the States. I thought your talks went on to the end of the week.'

Joshua let her break free suddenly and she almost fell. 'Someone else has taken my place,' he said briefly.

She stared at him. Could anyone else take Joshua Brett's place? Had something really dreadful happened? Something even he didn't know how to tell her?

'Is it Jayne?' Her voice trembled and he frowned. 'Is

she all right?' Kelly added. What was the matter with the man? Perhaps he was ill after all.

'Of course she's all right. Nothing's wrong, Kelly.' He stared at her almost without seeing. 'I've come a long way today, I'm tired, and I'm in no mood for an argument.' Then he remembered the snow and the road conditions and his anger returned again. 'You could have had an accident, no one would have known. I suppose you didn't tell the Rangers you were here?'

She shook her head, and he began pacing the room. The snow had melted and dried on his hair now, and he smoothed it back into place with long, unsteady fingers.

'I thought you were safe in Washington,' he went on, back and forth on the hearthrug—back and forth. 'I phoned, but the line was always engaged.'

'I left it off the hook. All your girl-friends kept ringing up. And that's why I came here,' she said more loudly, 'to get some peace, to get some reading done.'

'Peace? What's that?' His face was suddenly solemn, as if all the joy had gone out of his life for ever. 'I haven't had a moment's peace since I got on that plane for England.'

'That isn't my fault.' Just because he had business problems there was no need to take it out on her.

'Isn't it?' Then he came round the settee and grasped her by the shoulders. 'Then why haven't I been able to get you out of my mind for the past week? Why do I keep seeing those big amber eyes—why do I keep hearing your voice? . . .' He shook her, almost as if he wanted to shake himself. 'I couldn't think straight—I couldn't work properly . . .'

'And all your meetings?' muttered Kelly, hardly daring to believe what this meant—or where it would leave them.

'I left one of my London directors in charge. For once he could do a better job than I.' He still looked dazed, suffering from more than jet-lag. 'Don't you see what this means? I want you, Kelly. I've tried to fight it, but it won't let me go.'

'Then let me help you.' She gave him a shove and he

was so surprised that he took a step or two backwards.

'I didn't mean . . .' he began.

'Oh, yes you did. I'm very sorry that you've had a non-productive trip, but I'm sure the complaint is only temporary. This time next week I'll be back in London and you'll have forgotten all about me.'

For a moment she had thought a miracle was going to happen, but it had all gone wrong. He talked of wanting, not loving. And what self-respecting girl could give herself to a man who had fought against even *wanting* her?

'You don't realise, do you, even now?' He seemed to have difficulty finding his words. 'Kelly, I've—never felt like this about anyone before.'

'You loved Glenda.' The words that had to be said, somehow spoke themselves. If they surprised Kelly, they momentarily struck Joshua dumb.

'Yes,' he said eventually, and his voice sounded leaden.

Kelly stared at him, all her worst fear realised. And slowly an idea, that seemed to have been picking at her brain just lately, came to the forefront of her mind. 'Has this all been some—some revenge against the Osborns, by any chance?'

'Has—what—been a revenge?'

'I don't know.' She was shaking now, her mind all numb and cottonwool. 'Everything, I suppose. Wanting Jayne over here, being beastly to everyone, not giving Glenda her loan . . .'

'Is that what you really think?'

She shrugged.

'And why would I want to perpetrate this revenge?'

She looked down at her hands. 'You were in love with Glenda, you just admitted it. And Daddy stole her away. I would have thought that was reason enough.'

Joshua sighed wearily. 'He didn't steal Glenda— people are very rarely stolen, you know. Before she met your father she was already halfway lost.'

'Oh!' So Glenda had fallen out of love with him. But that didn't mean that he had fallen out of love with her.

'But why are we talking about Glenda? Why aren't we talking about why I travelled three thousand miles and then drove through a blizzard? Kelly,' he held out his hand, 'come over here.'

'No,' she said quickly, because there was a new tenderness about him and if she went over there she would be lost for ever. And she had thought it all out and she wasn't interested in becoming the Joshua-Brett-Girl-of-the-Year. Or would it be six months, or less?

As her mind grappled with the problem he noticed the pile of paperbacks in the corner of the settee. He bent down and picked one up. 'This degree thing? It's important to you?'

Her face tightened. 'It isn't a *thing*—and yes, it's important to me.'

He turned away, and she could sense a million thoughts rushing through his brain. When he turned back she knew that decisions had been made that she couldn't even guess at. All the doubt and uncertainty had gone from his eyes and were now replaced by quiet determination.

'Then we shall have to live in England,' he said, almost matter-of-factly.

The room spun and there was nothing for her to hang on to. Kelly swayed, and he raced round the settee and caught her.

'You're mad!' she muttered at last.

Joshua's lips quirked. 'Very probably.'

'Why England?' which wasn't what she meant to say. She meant, 'Why *we*?' but it didn't come out that way.

'If you want to finish this particular degree course— then we don't have any alternative, do we?' His hands were gentle on her arms now, and his thumbs were caressing little circles.

'I don't understand,' and it was true, because she didn't understand anything any more.

He smiled wickedly. 'You will when you get to know me better.' And then his face was serious once more. 'I may be prepared to put up with a full-time student for a wife—but I'm not prepared to see her only in the vacation.'

Kelly's eyes widened in her suddenly pale face. 'But what about the company? Surely you have to stay in Washington . . .' Again it wasn't what she had intended to say. She meant to repeat 'wife'—but she was frightened that her words might chase the beautiful bubble away.

'I've been here six years,' he reminded her. 'And I've got a good organisation going on both sides of the Atlantic. It will make very little difference if I live here and commute to England, or vice-versa. If you need to live in England, Kelly, then that's where we'll be. For the next couple of years, at least. Afterwards, I might need someone with new ideas in personnel management. Think about it. I might even be prepared to put up with a part-time working wife.'

'Oh!' He made it sound so easy—but instinct told her it wasn't. There would have to be a great many changes made for him to switch bases at almost a moment's notice. She fidgeted in his arms and he released her. His eyes were dark and watchful, never leaving her own.

'I—haven't said yes yet.'

'So I've noticed.'

'I thought you didn't like me much,' she whispered.

'Like?' he repeated. 'I think I almost hated you. When you first came it was bad enough—imagining all those other men . . . But here at Christmas, when I was beginning to think you were falling in love with me . . . It knocked me sideways, Kelly, when I found out the truth, because I didn't know where the lies began, or ended . . .'

'I know,' she whispered again.

'And you do love me, don't you?'

She nodded.

'And I love you, darling, almost from the beginning. Let's go and sit down and I'll tell you all about it.'

They snuggled up on the settee together, keeping very close, almost frightened that the other one would disappear if they moved too far away.

'Do you remember that first morning I drove you

into D.C. to see the sights?' he began, in that rich, wonderful voice that she now knew so well. 'We were in the hall putting on our coats, and you smiled at me.' He laughed quietly to himself. 'I don't think you were being particularly friendly, but it was the most bewitching, captivating, adorable smile . . .'

She peeped up at him. 'Was it?'

They kissed.

'And shall I tell you when you fell in love with me?' he went on, after quite a long time.

'All right,' she agreed. He looked so terribly pleased with himself. The fatigue in his face had almost vanished, only his eyes showed any tiredness. She tried to work out the number of hours he had been up—and the miles he had travelled just to be with her . . . Space Design had taken a back seat; it was still incredible to imagine.

'Then I'll tell you,' Joshua began again. 'It was here, wasn't it? That day of the bird-count and the ice storm. We saw that grouse and laughed at him.'

He tousled her hair and kissed her again. 'So you see, I win—I loved you first.' He tilted his dark handsome head sideways. 'Right?'

Wrong, she thought, because suddenly they weren't in America in winter and it wasn't today, but a summer's afternoon when they still had the house in Surrey and Glenda had only just married their father. It was Sunday afternoon tea under the chestnut tree. Glenda had worn a flimsy dress and floppy straw hat and had looked like someone in an advertisement for a French aperitif. Stuart Osborn had looked pleased with himself, as well he might, with his daughters and new wife around him. Jayne had been almost grown up, very lively, Kelly remembered, and Joshua had come to say goodbye to them all before leaving for America. Suddenly Kelly felt the same pain again, only now she recognised it as the pain of loving Joshua even then, and knowing she would never see him again . . . And now it was a December afternoon in a London flat overlooking Hampstead Heath. There was just Jayne and Kelly and a letter and

ticket from America. *'You're not going, of course.'* Her
words returned as if she had spoken them a minute ago,
and suddenly Kelly knew that she hadn't planned this
venture to help Jayne or Glenda, but because she had
loved Joshua ever since that summer's afternoon—and
the opportunity of seeing him again was just too important to be missed.

The fire crackled and a flurry of snow hit the
window. She smiled up from the protection of his
arms. 'Yes,' she whispered, 'you win,' but as he drew
her close again he didn't see the secret little smile on
her lips.

'Ouch, you're freezing!'

There was a cold draught as the bedcovers moved.
'Warm me up, then,' Joshua said in her ear, and she
gasped again as long, icy legs coiled around her own.

'Morning, crosspatch.' His eyes were unbelievably soft
and gentle as they gazed down at her. He gave her a
long, slow, sensuous kiss and trailed a light caress down
the whole length of her body. 'Now, are you going to
drink this tea I've so lovingly got up and made?'

Kelly nuzzled his chin. 'In a minute.'

'The fire's gone out,' he said, and they both laughed.
'I mean the one in the grate.'

Her eyes gazed up at him wickedly. Her body was
possessed of a new languorousness, yet in spite of it, or
maybe because of it, she felt last night's excitement twist
inside her again. Her hands smoothed the long, hard
column of his naked back and her senses whirled—remembering ... 'I can't imagine why you let the fire go
out—how are we going to keep warm?'

'I'll show you how,' he muttered thickly, pulling the
covers right over their heads. It was all dark, and
warmth and movement ... and their breath came in
little interrupted gasps of pleasure.

'Tea—come on, before it freezes in the cup,' and they
struggled up and reached for their mugs. He put his
sweater round her, his eyes feasting on the smooth white
curves that remained naked and inviting.

He bent his head and kissed the rosy tip of each breast.

'Josh . . .' and when his tongue flicked against her she gasped and resisted the temptation to hold him fast against her. 'Josh, listen,' and he sat up again, his tea unspilt in one hand. 'Josh . . .'

'That's three times you've said it. I'm listening, love, but be quick.' His strong features were suddenly taut and she could feel a certain tension mounting inside him. Her own body responded, but she tried to ignore it. Instead she sipped her tea, trying to think of how to say it.

'About Glenda,' she said at last.

He sighed. 'You're obsessed with that woman.'

'Why did you lose her?' Kelly tried to speak lightly. 'If you loved her . . .' she broke off, unable to imagine anyone refusing Joshua's love for more than a minute.

He shrugged. 'We were going to get married, we talked about it . . . but she didn't want to wait. I was just starting out with Space Design—the last thing I needed was a wife right then.' They looked at each other and he tried to smile. 'I know what you're thinking—and you're right. If I'd really loved her nothing would have stood in our way.'

'Not even important business conferences in other countries,' she said quietly.

He grinned properly this time and kissed her. 'Not even that, my love. But I didn't know that at the time. It felt like love . . .'

'And she hurt you—by refusing to wait?'

He nodded.

'And you sure as hell weren't going to get mixed up with an Osborn woman again,' she mimicked.

His eyes appreciated her understanding. 'Or any other woman, come to that . . . except for certain purposes . . .' If they hadn't both still been holding their tea, Kelly would have hit him.

'But you're long over it now,' she went on. 'I mean, you don't hold it against her?'

'Lord, no. Best thing she did for both of us—and I think she made your father reasonably happy.'

Kelly nodded. 'So—well, if you're not cross with her—er—don't you think you could change your mind about not lending her the money?' She broke off as he laughed outright.

'We're not even married yet and the woman's already trying to change me!'

Kelly blushed. 'I'm not.'

'Good. Don't try.'

'But, Joshua . . .' she began again.

'I like it when you call me Josh.'

Anything to placate him. 'Josh, *darling* . . .'

'Easy.' His voice was a husky drawl, then more firmly, 'I'm not lending Glenda the money to go into partnership with her latest shady boy-friend, and that's final, Kelly. Wife or no wife, you're not going to make me change my mind.'

She put her mug down on the floor. 'So what's going to happen to Jayne when Glenda sells the London flat?'

'Is she?' Joshua frowned, putting his own mug back on the floor.

Kelly put his sweater on properly, it was warmer and it would stop him looking at her with those dark, greedy eyes.

'She'll have to sell now; how else will she raise the money? Then where will Jayne live?' Then she remembered the way her sister had talked just before setting off for Florida. 'Or have you some plan for Jayne to stay on in America?' she asked, with a sudden chill clamping over her breast.

Joshua's smouldering eyes flashed with anger. 'That's right,' he drawled. 'I'd planned to set her up in a little flat in Washington, so that when I came over here on business trips she would be ready and waiting with open arms . . .'

'Josh!' Kelly muttered tearfully, and he grabbed her by the shoulders and gave her a little shake.

'You silly, silly girl.' Then his ready anger vanished as quickly as it had appeared. '*I'm* going to buy the blessed beauty farm—and Glenda and Jayne can manage it. *If* they can sort themselves out. That's why

I've sent Jayne down to Florida.'

'Oh!'

'Yes—you might well say "oh", my girl. Now, is there anything else you might like to know? Or can I start making love to you again?'

She looked down at the bedclothes. 'But why did you do it—spend all that money, if——?'

'If I don't still love Glenda,' he finished for her. He sighed when she nodded. 'Because I promised your father,' and at that Kelly swivelled round and knelt in front of him. Automatically he put the bedcover over her bare legs to keep them warm. 'Your father knew he was ill a couple of months before he died. We had a long talk, and he asked me to keep an eye on you all. Nothing legal. In fact, I think he assumed I would marry Glenda—but it didn't work out that way. Trouble was, I was so damned wrapped up with Space Design that I didn't see what was happening to Jayne. I *should* have seen, Kelly, maybe it's not too late . . .'

She squeezed his hand, how could she possibly have doubted him? Yet there was still something.

'That girl at the carol-singing,' she began slowly, 'the attractive brunette with her hair piled up. Is her name Jean?'

He frowned for a moment. 'Do you mean Barbara?' Then he seemed to follow her drift. 'She's one of my secretaries—lovely girl. Her husband's a pilot, she spends quite a bit of time on her own. Has three lovely children—very happily married . . .'

'Oh,' Kelly said again. That was all she seemed to be able to say lately. 'So—er—who's Jean?'

'I don't know any Jean.' So Kelly reminded him of the phone call he had received one evening before taking the brief trip to England. *'Oh,'* it was catching, *'that* Jean.' His eyes were tormenting and loving at the same time. 'She's one of my accounting team. We were sorting out the finances for Glenda's project. Jean's another lovely girl—very happily married.' Then his eyes grew serious. 'But all the women in my life aren't happily married, or even married at all,' he said carefully. 'In fact

I know two young ladies who are going to be quite upset when they hear about you.'

'Only two?' she queried with surprise.

'And that's quite enough to cope with, let me assure you,' he responded smartly.

'Are they both here in Washington?'

He shook his head. 'One here—the other in London.'

Her eyes sparkled. 'You beast!'

'Well, I always believe in good organisation.'

They laughed together. 'I'm sorry,' Kelly began, 'for making a fuss.'

'You're not—I understand. I still remember what it felt like when I thought you knew all those other men.'

He was jealous! Even if it was unfounded. How many more miracles would she discover today?

For the next few minutes they occupied themselves quite happily without any words.

'If we're not going to live in Washington,' said Kelly, when they both had to draw breath, 'we don't really need the house in Mclean. Couldn't you sell it?'

Joshua's shrewd eyes studied her face for a long time. 'You don't like the house, do you?'

'It's very beautiful.'

'But it reminds you of my past.'

She nodded.

'No, love, we keep the house—for the time being anyway. I'll need somewhere when I come over—and we shall both need it for holidays. And even if we did move, don't you know that my past will always come with us?'

She glanced up at him through her thick lashes and his face was serious and calm, yet equally determined. 'As my wife you'll have to get used to meeting women I've known—some intimately. I know it feels as if it hurts now, but it won't in time. After all,' he said, giving her such a ravishing smile that her heart sang, 'you didn't disapprove of my experience last night. Believe me, darling, you wouldn't want it any other way.'

With a flood of memory, their night of lovemaking became as tangible as if it was happening right now.

Joshua's possession had been so tender yet so passionate, and he had driven her remorselessly towards such heights of unbelievable rapture.

Kelly felt her face flush. 'I don't know how you did it,' she whispered mischievously. 'I thought you said you were tired.'

'You'd better be thankful that I was, my little love, otherwise I doubt I would have had the patience to hang on so long.' He tousled her hair and kissed the tip of her nose. 'You've got a lot to learn about men—and about love, and I've a feeling the finding out is going to be a bit difficult and prickly for both of us.' He kissed her crestfallen face again. 'But just think of all the kissing and making up!'

He made to take her in his arms again, but she wriggled out of his reach.

'I have to go somewhere,' she muttered, running for the bathroom, where she wiped the tears running haphazardly down her face. She didn't know why she was crying, nor how to explain it, so a brief escape was the answer. Afterwards, she washed her face and almost hugged herself with the joy of having found Joshua's incredible love. It would be difficult sometimes, she guessed he was right, but she knew she didn't want her life to be any other way.

Coming back into the room, she tiptoed to the window and peeped between the curtains. Then she pulled them wide open so that Joshua could see. Snow was piled up in the porch in a deep drift. It came halfway up the window and would be leaning heavily against the door.

'We're snowed in,' she said, scurrying back to bed.

'What a pity.' His eyes were all over her as she pulled off the sweater and snuggled down under the covers.

'Ouch,' he laughed, 'you're freezing!'

'I know.' Her teeth were chattering as he drew her into his arms—and the magic began.

'By the way,' he said, propping himself up on his elbow and smiling seriously down at her, 'you still haven't said if you'll marry me.'

Kelly coiled her arms around his neck and hoped that all the love she felt for him was shining in her eyes. 'Yes, please,' she said, 'I'd like very much to marry you.' And as his face relaxed she pulled him urgently down on top of her.

He roused her easily, and once again took her in quiet, firm possession.

Kelly's deep sigh froze on her lips for a glorious second.

'Warm now?' Joshua whispered.

She licked her lips. 'Oh, yes!'

He groaned softly. 'Love you.'

She moved restlessly beneath him, but he coaxed her still. 'Love you too,' she said quickly, on a tiny breath. How did he do it? How did he make it so wonderful again? She flattened her palms and slid them firmly down his back, and his slow, steady caress deepened as she arched nearer.

'Easy, darling,' he whispered, as she moaned, and to smooth away her little frown he gave her a long, gentle kiss.

'Josh . . .' she pleaded at last, and felt his lips smile against her cheek.

'Now, darling?'

'Yes, please.'

'Sure?'

'*Yes.*'

And then there wasn't time or breath for any more words . . . At this moment last night, Joshua had folded her in his arms and made exquisite, gentle love to her until she had cried softly with the sweetness of it all. But now his mood changed. He bit her ear—his lips hardened on her neck, and the muscles down his back tightened in masculine aggression.

Kelly gasped with excitement and felt her own passion rising . . . And this time they took the storm together; their sharp cries of joy piercing the brilliant blue stillness of the icy mountain air.

Romance for Mother's Day

You love Mills & Boon romances. So will your mother. The Mills & Boon Mother's Day Gift Pack is published on February 11th in the UK. It contains four new Mills & Boon paperback romances, in a most attractive presentation case:

Distrust her Shadow — Jessica Steel
Man with Two Faces — Jane Corrie
One Man Woman — Jessica Ayre
My Lord Kasseem — Mons Daveson

It's on sale where you buy paperbacks. £3.80 (UK net)

Mills & Boon
The rose of romance

FREE-an exclusive Anne Mather title, MELTING FIRE

At Mills & Boon we value very highly the opinion of our readers. What <u>you</u> tell us about what you like in romantic reading is important to us.

So if you will tell us which Mills & Boon romance you have most enjoyed reading lately, we will send you a copy of MELTING FIRE by Anne Mather – absolutely FREE.

There are no snags, no hidden charges. It's absolutely FREE.

Just send us your answer to our question, and help us to bring you the best in romantic reading.

CLAIM YOUR FREE BOOK NOW

Simply fill in details below, cut out and post to: Mills & Boon Reader Service, FREEPOST, P.O. Box 236, Croydon, Surrey CR9 9EL.

The Mills & Boon story I have most enjoyed during the past 6 months is:

TITLE _____

AUTHOR_____ BLOCK LETTERS, PLEASE

NAME (Mrs/Miss) _____ EP4

ADDRESS _____

_____ POST CODE _____

Offer restricted to ONE Free Book a year per household. Applies only in U.K. and Eire.
CUT OUT AND POST TODAY – NO STAMP NEEDED.

Mills & Boon
the rose of romance